JOHN I. JOHNSON, JR.
NEUROPHYSIOLOGY LABORATORIES
MEDICAL SCIENCES BUILDING
THE UNIVERSITY OF WISCONSIN
MADISON 6, WISCONSIN

A CLASSIFICATION OF
LIVING ANIMALS

A CLASSIFICATION OF LIVING ANIMALS

LORD ROTHSCHILD
G.M., Sc.D., F.R.S.

JOHN WILEY AND SONS INC.
New York, N.Y.

PUBLISHED THROUGHOUT THE WORLD, EXCEPT THE
UNITED STATES AND CANADA BY LONGMANS GREEN AND CO LTD

PRINTED IN GREAT BRITAIN
BY ROBERT MACLEHOSE AND CO LTD, THE UNIVERSITY PRESS, GLASGOW

CONTENTS

INTRODUCTION

The following notes may be helpful:

(1) Chapter I explains the purpose of the book and how to use it.

(2) Chapter II is a summarized classification of living animals.

(3) Chapter III is a classification of living animals, with examples of genera in each class, order, sub-order, etc.

(4) Appendix I provides references for further reading.

(5) Appendix II is a list of the authorities consulted on the classifications.

(6) Some 4,000 examples of 'better known' genera are mentioned in Chapter III and the Index, which also gives the order or sub-order to which each genus belongs.

(7) The Index contains more examples than the text. The reader who wishes to see whether a particular animal is classified should refer to the Index and not to the order, in Chapter III, to which he believes the animal belongs.

(8) Only a certain number of English names are recorded and some of these might be questioned by the purist. Innumerable examples could be given of the confusion caused by the use of vernacular as opposed to Latin names. Where I live, the hedgehog, *Erinaceus*, is sometimes called an urchin. Where I often work, an urchin is called *Echinus*. But members of the order Echinoida (sea urchins), to which *Echinus* belongs, are also called sea hedgehogs, egg urchins, sea eggs, egg-fish, buttonfish, sea thistles, needle shells, chestnuts, burrs, spikes, zarts, porcupines and whore's eggs.

(9) No species are given, only genera. The English names of some better known animals are, therefore, missing, because they refer to a species and not the genus: for example, the herring gull (*Larus argentatus*) and the crested newt (*Triton cristatus*). The reader will not find herring gull or crested newt in the Index, but will find gull, newt, *Larus* and *Triton*.

R.

I. SCOPE

DURING my studies of spermatozoa, I have often been frustrated by having to consult a number of books, instead of one, to find an up-to-date classification of the animal kingdom: and it occurred to me that other scientists might have the same difficulty. Classifications of the animal kingdom are available; but the only comprehensive ones of which I am aware are that of my first biology teacher, D. M. Reid (1925), which is out of print and now out-of-date, and that prepared in 1949 for Section F of the American Association for the Advancement of Science, *Zoological Names, a List of Phyla, Classes and Orders.* Apart from having no table of contents, index or examples, this pamphlet, which is reproduced in Spector's *Handbook of Biological Data* (1956), was clearly written for zoologists and not for physiologists, biochemists, biophysicists and those biologists who are not familiar with the classification of animals, for whom this book is intended.

The book and its Index can be used to find out how the animal kingdom, or parts of it, are classified, which are the eutherian mammals, what phasmids and Homoptera are, etc. Neither the book nor its Index can necessarily provide answers to questions about the systematic positions of individual genera, because there are some two hundred thousand genera in the animal kingdom.[1] Nevertheless, the Latin and some English names of a number of better known genera have been included. A genus may be well known to one person and unknown to another; any selection of 'better known genera' is bound, therefore, to be arbitrary. The reader is, therefore, almost certain to find that some genera, which are well known to him, are absent. Similarly, the English names of some better known animals are missing, because no species, only genera, are mentioned.

No extinct groups are mentioned, although from time to time members of such groups turn out not to be extinct at all, as in the case of the coelacanth (Actinistia) and the mollusc *Neopilina* (Tryblidiacea). The omission of extinct orders may give the misleading impression that a system of classification is top-heavy. In classifications of recent birds (Class Aves), for example, one sub-class, Neornithes, is sometimes included; this may seem unnecessary. But if the classification includes extinct birds, Neornithes is seen to be one of two sub-classes, the other, extinct, one being Archaeornithes.

Alternative classifications are given of the Parazoa (=Porifera), Platyhelminthes and Nematoda. The nematode classification of Chitwood & Chitwood (1950) is preferred to that of Hyman, which is well known because her treatise *The Invertebrates* (1940–1959) is so well known. A classification of the Parazoa by Dr. Maurice Burton is preferred to that of Hyman. Professor Jean Baer's classification of the Platyhelminthes, as yet unpublished, is preferred to that of Dr. Ben Dawes, but in this case, the decision was a personal one. The preferred classification is given first in each case. The same genera are cited as examples in the alternative classifications, but in the Index, genera are referred to the preferred classification. Alternative classifications of several other groups could have been given, e.g. the class Echinoidea, because systematics is a dynamic subject about which zoologists often disagree. But only the Parazoa, Platyhelminthes and Nematoda seemed to require this treatment in a book of this size and detail.

If an English name applies to a particular genus, as in the case of 'whelk', it will be found in the singular after the generic name, *Buccinum.* But if the same English name applies to two or more genera, it will be found, in the plural, after the genera to which it applies, for example *Cavolina, Limacina* (sea-butterflies). When English names are available for higher groupings, such as sponges (Parazoa), these will be found after the Latin names. No attempt has been made to give a comprehensive list of English or vernacular names, interesting as it may be to know that everyone in the Barbados is familiar with sea eggs, but no one with sea urchins. Such information is outside the scope of this book. Whenever possible, therefore, Latin and not English names should be looked up in the Index. In a few cases where an animal causes a disease which has an English name, it has been put in brackets after the generic name of the animal, for example *Entamoeba* (amoebic dysentery).

[1] If a genus is not in this book, the most likely place to find it is in Neave's *Nomenclator Zoologicus* (1939–1950).

When a synonym exists for a phylum, class, order, etc. and is worth mentioning, it is put in brackets after the preferred name, e.g.

DISCOCEPHALI (= ECHENEIFORMES)

If the group represented by the synonym is approximately equal to the group represented by the preferred name, the sign for 'approximately equal' is used:

PLECTOGNATHI ($\doteqdot$ TETRAODONTIFORMES)

If there are two synonyms, they are recorded as follows:

OLIGONEOPTERA (= ENDOPTERYGOTA, HOLOMETABOLA)

When the relationship between a preferred name and certain synonyms or near-synonyms is simple, the relationship is recorded as follows, sometimes as a footnote:

MESOGASTROPODA (= MONOTOCARDIA, PECTINIBRANCHIA, − STENOGLOSSA)

This means that the order Mesogastropoda is the same as the order Monotocardia or Pectinibranchia, *minus* Stenoglossa. A plus sign between two synonyms would have the analogous meaning.

Synonyms of genera have only been given where there was good reason to do so. To attempt more would make several entries under orders and sub-orders cumbersome. For example, the palmate newt *Triturus helveticus* (Caudata) is, or has been, known as *Diemictylus palmatus*, *Molge palmata* and *Triton palmatus*, so that the inclusion of these synonyms would be entered as follows:

Triturus (= *Diemictylus, Molge, Triton*) (newt)

Even if such an entry were desirable in principle, it would be unacceptable in practice, because the synonyms apply to the palmate newt and not necessarily to all newts. This question, of a synonym often applying to one species and not to the whole genus, is another reason for avoiding synonyms except when they serve a special purpose.

Some synonyms, such as *Troglodytes* for *Pan* (the chimpanzee), *Auchenia* for *Lama* (the llama) and a few others, may be thought surprising or unnecessary. They have been included because some physiologists or biochemists used these synonyms instead of the preferred names.

To avoid possible confusion, I have occasionally put a warning footnote when the name of a group, such as Decapoda, is used in more than one part of the animal kingdom. Attention has not been drawn to cases of two different animals having, or having had, the same names. A casual glance at Neave's *Nomenclator Zoologicus* (1939–1950) shows that homonyms are far more common than many biologists realize. *Aricia*, for example, is cited in Neave as a mollusc, a polychaete, a fly and a moth. There seemed no point in trying to record all homonyms, irrespective of their importance for readers of this book.

Apart from 'phylum', 'class', 'order', etc., the Index contains all the words in Chapters II and III. If the reader wishes to look up Mammalia, or Prototheria, or Simiae in the Index, no difficulties arise and the appropriate page numbers will be found after these words, for example, Prototheria, 43. But if the reader wishes to know the systematic position of *Phascolarctos*, a page number would provide insufficient information because there are about seventy-five Latin or English generic names per page. In the Index, therefore, the generic name of an animal, or the English name of a genus, is followed by the order or sub-order (when these exist) to which the animal belongs, and then the page number, as in the following examples:

Phascolarctos, Marsupialia, 44
three-toed sloth (*Bradypus*), Edentata, 44

It is hardly necessary to mention that if two page numbers occur after a word in the Index, as in

Acoela, 13, 22

the Acoela will be found on both pages. This is because Acoela is an order within the class Turbellaria (phylum Platyhelminthes) and within the class Gastropoda (phylum Mollusca).

I referred on page 2 to the inclusion in the Index of animals mentioned in a number of textbooks of physiology and biochemistry. The format of this book prevents all of these being referred to in the text, even if this were desirable, and a number have, therefore, been mentioned only in the Index. In such cases the entry is of the form

Eriocheir, Reptantia, 31

The entry shows to which sub-order *Eriocheir* belongs, while reference to p. 31 shows that *Eriocheir* is a crustacean and not a mollusc.[1] If, therefore, a reader wants to look up a particular genus in this book, reference *must*, in the first instance, be made to the Index and not to the text, as more animals are mentioned in the former than the latter. No English names are given of genera which are only mentioned in the Index.

All the classifications have been discussed with specialists on the group or groups in question. To avoid cluttering up this chapter with innumerable acknowledgements to the many scientists who have had the kindness and patience to help me, an Acknowledgement Appendix is included at the end of this book. In fairness to those who have helped me, I should own that I have not always taken their advice. Any errors[2] are, therefore, my responsibility and due to ignorance of a diverting branch of natural science which is neglected by many 'modern' biologists.

Since my book is, in a sense, a dictionary, I will conclude this chapter with some observations made by a previous lexicographer (Johnson, 1755, A[r]).

'It is the fate of those who toil at the lower employments of life, to be rather driven by the fear of evil, than attracted by the prospect of good; to be exposed to censure, without hope of praise; to be disgraced by miscarriage, or punished for neglect, where success would have been without applause, and diligence without reward.

'Among these unhappy mortals is the writer of dictionaries; whom mankind have considered, not as the pupil, but the slave of science, the pionier of literature, doomed only to remove rubbish and clear obstructions from the paths of Learning and Genius, who press forward to conquest and glory, without bestowing a smile on the humble drudge that facilitates their progress. Every other authour may aspire to praise; the lexicographer can only hope to escape reproach, and even this negative recompense has been yet granted to very few.'

---

[1] Reptantia is a sub-order of Decapoda (Crustacea); but Decapoda is also a sub-order of Dibranchia (Mollusca).

[2] This book is certain to contain errors and misprints. I should be most grateful if readers would let me know when they detect them.

II. SUMMARIZED CLASSIFICATION

THE *approximate* number of described species in each group is given in the second column. Numbers followed by an asterisk differ greatly from those given by Mayr, Linsley & Usinger (1953).

Phylum PROTOZOA	30,000	*page*	6
MESOZOA	50		9
PARAZOA	4,200		9
CNIDARIA	9,600		11
CTENOPHORA	80		12
PLATYHELMINTHES	15,000*		13
NEMERTINA	550		16
ASCHELMINTHES			
Class Rotifera	1,500		17
Gastrotricha	140		17
Echinoderida	100		17
Priapulida	5		17
Nematomorpha	250		17
Nematoda	10,000		17
Phylum ACANTHOCEPHALA	300		20
ENTOPROCTA	60		20
POLYZOA	4,000		20
PHORONIDA	15*		20
BRACHIOPODA	260		21
MOLLUSCA	100,000		21
SIPUNCULOIDEA	275		23
ECHIUROIDEA	80		23
ANNELIDA	7,000		24
ARTHROPODA			
Class Onychophora	73		24
Pauropoda ⎤			24
Diplopoda ⎟			24
Chilopoda ⎬ 9,400			25
Symphyla ⎦			25
Insecta	700,000		25
Crustacea	25,000		29
Merostomata	4		31
Arachnida	30,000		31
Pycnogonida	440		31
Pentastomida	60		32
Tardigrada	280		32
Phylum CHAETOGNATHA	50*		32
POGONOPHORA	43*		32
ECHINODERMATA	5,700		32
CHORDATA			
Sub-phylum Hemichordata	91		34
Urochordata	1,600		34
Cephalochordata	13		35

Vertebrata

Class Marsipobranchii		35
Selachii	23,000	35
Bradyodonti		36
Pisces		36
Amphibia	2,000	40
Reptilia	5,000	41
Aves	8,590	41
Mammalia	4,500	43

III. CLASSIFICATION OF LIVING ANIMALS

Phylum **PROTOZOA**

Class **MASTIGOPHORA**
  (=FLAGELLATA)

Sub-class **PHYTOMASTIGINA**
  (=PHYTOFLAGELLATA)

Order **PHYTOMONADINA**
  (=VOLVOCINA)
  *Carteria; Chlorogonium; Chlamydomonas;
  Haematococcus; Eudorina; Pandorina; Volvox;
  Polytoma*

Order **XANTHOMONADINA**
  Chloramoeba; Myxochloris; Rhizochloris

Order **CHLOROMONADINA**
  Gonyostomum; Vacuolaria

Order **EUGLENOIDINA**
  Euglena; Trachelomonas; Phacus; Peranema

Order **CRYPTOMONADINA**
  Chilomonas; Cryptomonas; Cyathomonas

Order **DINOFLAGELLATA**
  (=PERIDINEAE)
  *Haplodinium; Blastodinium; Ceratium;
  Dinamoebidium; Gymnodinium; Noctiluca;
  Peridinium*

Order **EBRIIDEAE**
  (=EBRIACEAE)
  Ebria; Hermesinum

Order **SILICOFLAGELLATA**
  Dictyocha

Order **COCCOLITHOPHORIDA**
  Calyptrosphaera; Acanthosolenia

Order **CHRYSOMONADINA**
  *Chromulina; Mallomonas; Oicomonas; Uroglena;
  Chrysamoeba; Dinobryon; Hydrurus;
  Dendromonas; Ochromonas*

Sub-class **ZOOMASTIGINA**
  (=ZOOFLAGELLATA)

Order **PROTOMONADINA**
  Monosiga; Leptomonas; Crithidia; Leishmania
  (kala-azar, oriental sore); *Trypanosoma* (sleeping-
  sickness, nagana, etc.); *Schizotrypanum* (Chagas'
  disease, etc.); *Bodo*

Order **METAMONADINA**
  (=POLYMASTIGINA + HYPERMASTIGINA)
  Enteromonas; Monocercomonas (=Eutrichomastix);
  *Hexamastix; Devescovina; Trichomonas;
  Embadomonas; Chilomastix; Lophomonas;
  Trimastix; Trichonympha*

6

Order **DISTOMATINA**
    (= Diplomonadida)
    Hexamita; Giardia
Order **OPALININA**
    Cepedea; Opalina; Zelleriella

Class **RHIZOPODA**
  (= Sarcodina)

Order **RHIZOMASTIGINA**
    (= Pantostomatida)
    Mastigamoeba; Histomonas (blackhead of poultry);
    Dientamoeba
Order **AMOEBINA**
    Amoeba; Chaos; Vahlkampfia; Endamoeba;
    Entamoeba (amoebic dysentery); *Endolimax;*
    Iodamoeba
Order **TESTACEA**
    Arcella; Centropyxis; Cochliopodium; Difflugia;
    Nebela; Penardia; Assulina; Chlamydophrys;
    Euglypha; Gromia; Arachnula; Biomyxa;
    Allogromia; Microgromia
Order **FORAMINIFERA**
    Discorbis; Elphidium (= *Polystomella*); *Globigerina;*
    Cornuspira; Peneroplis; Textularia; Nummulites;
    Planorbulina; Rotalia

Class **ACTINOPODA**

Order **RADIOLARIA**
    Acanthometra; Sphaerocapsa; Acanthosphaera;
    Collozoum; Sphaerozoum; Thalassicola;
    Aulacantha; Coelodendrum
Order **HELIOZOA**
    Actinophrys; Actinosphaerium; Actinolophus;
    Astrodisculus; Acanthocystis; Raphidiophrys;
    Actinomonas; Vampyrella; Clathrulina;
    Hedriocystis; Monomastigocystis

Class **SPOROZOA**
  (= Telosporidia)

Sub-class **GREGARINOMORPHA**

Order **ARCHIGREGARINA**
    Merogregarina; Selenidium; Selenocystis
Order **EUGREGARINA**
    Gonospora; Gregarina; Lecudina; Monocystis;
    Porospora; Stylocephalus
Order **SCHIZOGREGARINA**
    Caulleryella; Lipotropha; Machadoella;
    Ophryocystis; Schizocystis; Syncystis

Sub-class **COCCIDIOMORPHA**

Order **PROCOCCIDIA**
    Selenococcidium
Order **EUCOCCIDIA**
  Sub-order Adeleidea
    Adelina; Klossia; Karyolysus; Hepatozoon;
    Haemogregarina
  Sub-order Eimeriidea
    Cyclospora; Isospora; Eimeria (= *Coccidium*);
    Globidium; Merocystis

Sub-order HAEMOSPORIDIA
Haemoproteus; Leucocytozoon; Plasmodium (malaria); *Babesia* (=*Piroplasma*) (Texas cattle fever, etc.); *Theileria* (African East Coast cattle fever)

SPOROZOA whose systematic position is uncertain

Toxoplasma (toxoplasmosis); *Sarcocystis* (sarcosporidiosis); *Helicosporidium*

Class **CNIDOSPORIDIA**
(=NEMATOCYSTIDA, NEOSPORIDIA, AMOEBOSPORIDIA)

Order **MYXOSPORIDIA**
Ceratomyxa; Leptotheca; Chloromyxum; Sphaerospora; Coccomyxa; Henneguya; Myxidium; Myxobolus; Myxosoma

Order **MICROSPORIDIA**
(=CRYPTOCYSTA)
Nosema; Glugea; Thelohania; Plistophora; Mrazekia; Telomyxa

Order **ACTINOMYXIDIA**
Guyenotia; Tetractinomyxon

Order **HAPLOSPORIDIA**
Haplosporidium

Class **CILIATA**
(=CILIOPHORA)

Sub-class **HOLOTRICHA**

Order **GYMNOSTOMATIDA**
Sub-order RHABDOPHORINA
Holophrya; Amphileptus; Dileptus
Sub-order CYRTOPHORINA
Chilodonella; Nassula; Prorodon

Order **SUCTORIDA**
(=ACINETA, TENTACULIFERA)
Podophrya; Acineta

Order **CHONOTRICHIDA**
(=PERITRICHA)
Spirochona

Order **TRICHOSTOMATIDA**
Coelosomides; Tillina; Colpoda; Balantidium (dysentery)

Order **HYMENOSTOMATIDA**
Sub-order TETRAHYMENINA
Tetrahymena; Glaucoma; Ichthyophthirius
Sub-order PENICULINA
Frontonia; Paramecium (slipper animalcule); *Urocentrum*
Sub-order PLEURONEMATINA
Pleuronema; Cyclidium

Order **ASTOMATIDA**
(=ANOPLOPHRYINEA)
Anoplophrya; Radiophrya; Haptophrya

Order **APOSTOMATIDA**
Foettingeria; Gymnodinioides; Ophiuraespira; Spirophrya

Order **THIGMOTRICHIDA**
Thigmophrya; Conchophthirus; Ancistrum; Boveria; Ancistrocoma; Hypocomella; Hypocoma
Order **PERITRICHIDA**
(=STOMATODA)
Vorticella; Epistylis; Zoothamnium; Trichodina; Urceolaria

Sub-class **SPIROTRICHA**

Order **HETEROTRICHIDA**
Sub-order HETEROTRICHINA
Climacostomum; Condylostoma; Spirostomum; Stentor
Sub-order LICNOPHORINA
Licnophora
Order **OLIGOTRICHIDA**
Strombidium; Halteria; Strombilidium
Order **TINTINNIDA**
Tintinnopsis; Tintinnus
Order **ENTODINIOMORPHIDA**
Epidinium; Entodinium; Ophryoscolex; Cycloposthium
Order **CTENOSTOMATIDA**
(=ODONTOSTOMATIDA)
Epalxis; Saprodinium; Discomorpha
Order **HYPOTRICHIDA**
Diophrys; Euplotes; Oxytricha; Uroleptus

Phylum **MESOZOA**[1]

Order **DICYEMIDA**
(=RHOMBOZOA)
Dicyema; Microcyema
Order **ORTHONECTIDA**
Rhopalura

Phylum **PARAZOA** (=PORIFERA, SPONGIIDA) (sponges)[2]

Class **NUDA**[3]

Order **CALCAREA**
(=CALCISPONGIAE)
Sub-order HOMOCOELA (ascon sponges)
Leucosolenia (=*Ascute*); *Clathrina*
Sub-order HETEROCOELA
Leucilla; Scypha (=*Sycon*); *Leuconia*
(=*Leucandra*); *Grantia* (=*Sycandra*)

---

[1] Members of this phylum are often considered to be degenerate members of phylum Platyhelminthes, pp. 13–14.
[2] Classification by Burton.
[3] Sometimes considered as a phylum, in which case phylum Parazoa becomes a sub-kingdom. Class Nuda also occurs in phylum Ctenophora, p. 13.

Order **HEXACTINELLIDA** (glass sponges)
  (=Triaxonida, Hyalospongiae)
Sub-order Hexasterophora
  Euplectella (Venus's flower basket); *Farrea;*
  Aphrocallistes
Sub-order Amphidiscophora
  Hyalonema; Pheronema; Monoraphis

Class **GELATINOSA**[1]

Order **TETRAXONIDA**
Sub-order Homosclerophora
  (≑Carnosa, Microsclerophora)
  Plakina; Oscarella; Bajulus; Hexadella; Thrombus
Sub-order Streptastrosclerophora
  Thenea
Sub-order Astrosclerophora
  Stelletta; Tethya; Chondrosia; Geodia; Tetilla
  (=*Craniella*); *Cliona; Spheciospongia* (loggerhead
  sponge); *Suberites*
Sub-order Sigmatosclerophora
  Myxilla; Halichondria; Haliclona (=*Chalina,*
  Halina); *Microciona; Esperiopsis; Adocia*
  (=*Reniera*); *Cladorhiza; Spongilla*
Order **KERATOSA**[2] (horny sponges)
  Spongia (=*Euspongia*) (bath sponge); *Halisarca;*
  Hircinia; Aplysina; Aplysilla

Phylum **PORIFERA** (=Spongiida, Parazoa) (sponges)[3]

Class **CALCAREA**
  (=Calcispongiae)

Order **ASCONOSA** (ascon sponges)
  (=Homocoela)
  Leucosolenia (=*Ascute*); *Clathrina*
Order **SYCONOSA**
  (=Heterocoela)
  Leucilla; Scypha (=*Sycon*); *Leuconia*
  (=*Leucandra*); *Grantia* (=*Sycandra*)

Class **HEXACTINELLIDA** (glass sponges)
  (=Triaxonida, Hyalospongiae)

Order **HEXASTEROPHORA**
  Euplectella (Venus's flower basket); *Farrea;*
  Aphrocallistes
Order **AMPHIDISCOPHORA**
  Hyalonema; Pheronema; Monoraphis

Class **DEMOSPONGIAE**

Sub-class **TETRACTINELLIDA**

Order **MYXOSPONGIDA**
  Halisarca; Oscarella; Bajulus; Hexadella; Thenea

---

[1] Sometimes considered as a phylum, in which case phylum Parazoa becomes a sub-kingdom.
[2] The systematics of this order requires revision.   [3] Alternative classification by Hyman (1940).

Order **CARNOSA**
(=Homosclerophora, Microsclerophora)
Plakina; Thrombus; Chondrosia; Haliclona
(=*Chalina, Halina*)
Order **CHORISTIDA**
Stelletta; Geodia; Tetilla (=*Craniella*)

Sub-class **MONAXONIDA**

Order **HADROMERINA**
(=Astromonaxonellida)
Cliona; Spheciospongia (loggerhead sponge);
Suberites
Order **HALICHONDRINA**
Halichondria
Order **POECILOSCLERINA**
Microciona; Myxilla; Esperiopsis; Cladorhiza
Order **HAPLOSCLERINA**
Adocia (=*Reniera*)*; Spongilla*
Order **EPIPOLASIDA**
Tethya

Sub-class **KERATOSA** (horny sponges)

Spongia (=*Euspongia*) (bath sponge); *Hircinia;*
Aplysina; Aplysilla

Phylum CNIDARIA (=Coelenterata – Ctenophora)

Class **HYDROZOA** (hydroids, medusae)
(=Hydromedusae)

Order **ATHECATA**
(=Gymnoblastea, Anthomedusae)
Hydra; Tubularia; Sarsia; Coryne; Velella (by-the-
wind-sailor); *Millepora; Hydractinia;*
Bougainvillia; Stylaster; Spirocodon
Order **THECATA**
(=Calyptoblastea, Leptomedusae)
Phialidium; Obelia; Aequorea; Halecium;
Sertularia; Plumularia
Order **LIMNOMEDUSAE**
Gonionemus; Craspedacusta; Olindias; Limnocnida
Order **TRACHYMEDUSAE**
Geryonia (=*Carmarina*)*; Liriope; Aglantha*
Order **NARCOMEDUSAE**
Solmissus; Aegina; Cunina
Order **SIPHONOPHORA**
Physalia (Portuguese man-of-war); *Halistemma;*
Lensia; Muggiaea; Agalma

Class **SCYPHOZOA** (jelly fish)
(=Scyphomedusae)

Order **STAUROMEDUSAE**
Lucernaria; Haliclystus
Order **CUBOMEDUSAE**
Carybdea; Chirodropus
Order **CORONATAE**
Atolla; Linuche; Nausithoe; Periphylla

Order **SEMAEOSTOMAE**
  Pelagia; Chrysaora; Cyanea; Aurelia (=Aurellia);
  Dactylometra
Order **RHIZOSTOMAE**
  Cassiopea; Rhizostoma; Cotylorhiza

Class **ANTHOZOA**

Sub-class **CERIANTIPATHARIA**

Order **ANTIPATHARIA** (black corals)
  Antipathes
Order **CERIANTHARIA**
  Cerianthus

Sub-class **OCTOCORALLIA** (soft corals)

Order **ALCYONACEA**
  Alcyonium (dead men's fingers)
Order **GORGONACEA**
  Eunicella (sea fan); *Gorgonia*
Order **PENNATULACEA**
  Pennatula (sea pen); *Virgularia*

Sub-class **ZOANTHARIA**

Order **ZOANTHINIARIA** (zoanthids)
  Zoanthus; Epizoanthus; Palythoa
Order **CORALLIMORPHARIA**
  Corynactis
Order **ACTINIARIA** (sea anemones)
  Anemonia (=Anthea); Actinia; Tealia; Metridium
  (=Actinoloba); Calliactis; Adamsia; Peachia
Order **PTYCHODACTIARIA**
  Ptychodactis
Order **SCLERACTINIA** (true corals, stony corals)
  Fungia; Porites; Acropora; Caryophyllia;
  Meandrina

Phylum **CTENOPHORA**
(=Coelenterata – Cnidaria) (comb jellies)

Class **TENTACULATA**

Order **CYDIPPIDA**
  Pleurobrachia (sea gooseberry); *Hormiphora*
Order **LOBATA**
  Leucothea (=Eucharis); Bolinopsis (=Bolina);
  Mnemiopsis (comb jelly)
Order **CESTIDA**
  (=Cestoidea)
  Cestum (=Cestus) (Venus's girdle); *Velamen*
  (=Vexillum, Folia)
Order **PLATYCTENEA**
  (=Ctenoplana)
  Ctenoplana; Coeloplana; Tjalfiella; Gastrodes

Class **NUDA**[1]

Order **BEROIDA**
Beroe

Phylum **PLATYHELMINTHES** (flatworms)[2]

Class **TURBELLARIA** (turbellarians)

Order **ACOELA**[3]
Aphanostoma; Convoluta

Order **RHABDOCOELA**
Catenula; Macrostomum; Dalyellia; Gyratrix; Paravortex

Order **ALLOEOCOELA**
Hofstenia; Plagiostomum; Otomesostoma; Monocelis

Order **TRICLADIDA**

Sub-order MARICOLA
Bdelloura; Uteriporus; Procerodes (=Gunda)

Sub-order PALUDICOLA
Planaria; Dugesia (=Euplanaria); Dendrocoelum

Sub-order TERRICOLA
Geoplana; Rhynchodemus; Bipalium

Order **POLYCLADIDA**

Sub-order ACOTYLEA
Stylochus; Notoplana; Cestoplana

Sub-order COTYLEA
Thysanozoon; Eurylepta; Prosthiostomum

Class **TEMNOCEPHALOIDEA**

Order **TEMNOCEPHALIDEA**
(=DACTYLIFERA, DACTYLODA)
Temnocephala

Class **MONOGENEA**
(=HETEROCOTYLEA)

Sub-class **MONOPISTHOCOTYLEA**

Order **CAPSALOIDEA**
Tristoma; Capsala

Order **UDONELLOIDEA**
Udonella

Order **GYRODACTYLOIDEA**
Gyrodactylus; Dactylogyrus

Order **ACANTHOCOTYLOIDEA**
Acanthocotyle

Order **PROTOGYRODACTYLOIDEA**
Protogyrodactylus

Sub-class **POLYOPISTHOCOTYLEA**

Order **CHIMAEROCOLOIDEA**
Callorhynchicola

Order **DICLIDOPHOROIDEA**
Diplozoon; Hexostoma; Mazocraes; Microcotyle; Gastrocotyle; Diclidophora; Discocotyle

See Parazoa, p. 9.   [2] Classification by Baer.   See Opisthobranchia, p. 22.

Order **DICLYBOTHROIDEA**
Diclybothrium
Order **POLYSTOMATOIDEA**
Polystoma; Hexabothrium

Class **CESTODARIA**

Order **AMPHILINIDEA**
Amphilina
Order **GYROCOTYLIDEA**
Gyrocotyle

Class **CESTODA** (tapeworms)

Sub-class **DIDESMIDA**

Order **PSEUDOPHYLLIDEA**
(=Bothriocephaloidea)
Diphyllobothrium (=Dibothriocephalus); Ligula;
Schistocephalus; Caryophyllaeus; Wenyonia

Sub-class **TETRADESMIDA**

Order **HAPLOBOTHRIOIDEA**
Haplobothrium
Order **TETRARHYNCHOIDEA**
(=Trypanorhyncha)
Tetrarhynchus; Floriceps; Tentacularia; Grillotia;
Hepatoxylon; Aporhynchus
Order **DIPHYLLIDEA**
Echinobothrium
Order **TETRAPHYLLIDEA**
(=Phyllobothrioidea)
Phyllobothrium; Acanthobothrium;
Echeneibothrium; Discocephalum
Order **LECANICEPHALOIDEA**
Lecanicephalum; Parataenia
Order **TETRABOTHRIOIDEA**
Tetrabothrius
Order **PROTEOCEPHALOIDEA**
Proteocephalus
Order **NIPPOTAENOIDEA**
Nippotaenia
Order **CYCLOPHYLLIDEA**
(=Taenioidea)
Bertiella; Raillietina; Dipylidium; Hymenolepis;
Taenia (=Cysticercus); Echinococcus;
Mesocestoides

Class **TREMATODA** (flukes)

Sub-class **ASPIDOGASTREA**
(=Aspidocotylea, Aspidobothria)

Aspidogaster

Sub-class **DIGENEA**
(=Malacocotylea)

Schistosoma (=Bilharzia); Bilharziella; Fasciola
(=Distoma, Distomum), Dicrocoelium (liver flukes,
cattle & sheep); *Parorchis; Paragonimus* (lung
fluke); *Bucephalus; Clonorchis* (Chinese liver fluke
disease); *Heterophyes; Paramphistomum* (cattle
rumen fluke); *Strigea; Diplostomum; Echinostoma*

Phylum PLATYHELMINTHES (flatworms)[1]

Class **TURBELLARIA** (turbellarians)
Order **ACOELA**
Aphanostoma; Convoluta
Order **RHABDOCOELA**
Catenula; Macrostomum; Dalyellia; Gyratrix;
Temnocephala; Paravortex
Order **ALLOEOCOELA**
Hofstenia; Plagiostomum; Otomesostoma;
Monocelis
Order **TRICLADIDA**
Sub-order MARICOLA
Bdelloura; Uteriporus; Procerodes (=Gunda)
Sub-order PALUDICOLA
Planaria; Dugesia (=Euplanaria); Dendrocoelum
Sub-order TERRICOLA
Geoplana; Rhynchodemus; Bipalium
Order **POLYCLADIDA**
Sub-order ACOTYLEA
Stylochus; Notoplana; Cestoplana
Sub-order COTYLEA
Thysanozoon; Eurylepta; Prosthiostomum

Class **TREMATODA** (flukes)
Order **MONOGENEA**
(=HETEROCOTYLEA)
Sub-order MONOPISTHOCOTYLEA
Gyrodactylus; Dactylogyrus; Protogyrodactylus;
Udonella; Tristoma; Capsala; Acanthocotyle
Sub-order POLYOPISTHOCOTYLEA
Hexabothrium; Polystoma; Mazocraes;
Discocotyle; Diclybothrium; Microcotyle;
Gastrocotyle; Callorhynchicola; Diclidophora;
Hexostoma; Diplozoon
Order **ASPIDOGASTREA**
(=ASPIDOCOTYLEA, ASPIDOBOTHRIA)
Aspidogaster
Order **DIGENEA**
(=MALACOCOTYLEA)
Sub-order GASTEROSTOMATA
Bucephalus
Sub-order PROSOSTOMATA
Dicrocoelium, Fasciola (=Distoma, Distomum)
(liver flukes, cattle & sheep); *Clonorchis* (Chinese
liver fluke disease); *Heterophyes; Paragonimus*
(lung fluke); *Paramphistomum* (cattle rumen fluke);
Strigea; Diplostomum; Echinostoma; Parorchis;
Schistosoma (=Bilharzia); Bilharziella

[1] Alternative classification by Dawes.

Class **CESTODA** (tapeworms)

Sub-class **CESTODARIA**

Order **AMPHILINIDEA**
Amphilina
Order **GYROCOTYLIDEA**
Gyrocotyle

Sub-class **EUCESTODA**

Order **PROTEOCEPHALA**
Proteocephalus
Order **TETRAPHYLLIDEA**
(=PHYLLOBOTHRIOIDEA)
Phyllobothrium; Acanthobothrium; Echeneibothrium
Order **LECANICEPHALA**
Parataenia; Lecanicephalum
Order **DISCULICEPITIDEA**
Discocephalum
Order **DIPHYLLIDEA**
Echinobothrium
Order **TRYPANORHYNCHA**
(=TETRARHYNCHOIDEA)
Tetrarhynchus; Floriceps; Tentacularia; Grillotia;
Hepatoxylon; Aporhynchus
Order **CYCLOPHYLLIDEA**
(=TAENIOIDEA)
Bertiella; Raillietina; Dipylidium; Hymenolepis;
Taenia (=Cysticercus); Echinococcus;
Mesocestoides; Tetrabothrius
Order **CARYOPHYLLIDEA**
Wenyonia; Caryophyllaeus
Order **NIPPOTAENIIDEA**
Nippotaenia
Order **PSEUDOPHYLLIDEA**
Ligula; Diphyllobothrium (=Dibothriocephalus);
Schistocephalus; Haplobothrium

Phylum **NEMERTINA** (=RHYNCHOCOELA) (ribbon worms)

Class **ANOPLA**

Order **PALAEONEMERTINA**
(=MESONEMERTINA)
Cephalothrix; Tubulanus
Order **HETERONEMERTINA**
Cerebratulus; Lineus (boot-lace worm)

Class **ENOPLA**

Order **HOPLONEMERTINA**
Sub-order MONOSTYLIFERA
Carcinonemertes; Amphiporus; Tetrastemma;
Geonemertes
Sub-order POLYSTYLIFERA
Drepanophorus; Pelagonemertes; Nectonemertes

Order **BDELLONEMERTINA**
(=Bdellomorpha)
Malacobdella

Phylum ASCHELMINTHES[1]

Class **ROTIFERA** (wheel animalcules)
(=Rotatoria)

Order **SEISONIDEA**
Seison
Order **BDELLOIDEA**
*Habrotrocha; Philodina; Rotaria (=Rotifer);
Adineta; Philodinavus (=Microdina)*
Order **MONOGONONTA**
Sub-order Ploima
*Brachionus; Keratella (=Anuraea); Epiphanes
(=Hydatina); Euchlanis; Lepadella (=Metopidia);
Lecane (=Cathypna, Distyla); Monostyla;
Notommata; Asplanchna*
Sub-order Flosculariacea
*Testudinella (=Pterodina); Filinia (=Triarthra);
Hexarthra (=Pedalia, Pedalion); Trochosphaera;
Floscularia (=Melicerta); Conochilus*
Sub-order Collothecacea
Collotheca (=Floscularia); Stephanoceros

Class **GASTROTRICHA**

Order **MACRODASYOIDEA**
Cephalodasys
Order **CHAETONOTOIDEA**
Neodasys; Chaetonotus

Class **ECHINODERIDA**
(=Kinorhyncha)

Centroderes; Echinoderes; Pycnophyes

Class **PRIAPULIDA**[2]

Priapulus; Halicryptus

Class **NEMATOMORPHA** (horse-hair worms)
(=Gordiacea)

Order **NECTONEMATOIDEA**
Nectonema
Order **GORDIOIDEA**
Chordodes; Gordius

Class **NEMATODA** (roundworms)[3]
(=Nemata)

Sub-class **PHASMIDIA**

Order **RHABDITIDA**
Sub-order Rhabditina
Rhabditis; Diplogaster; Cephalobus; Panagrellus
(sour paste eelworm); *Turbatrix* (vinegar eelworm);
Rhabdias (lung nematode); *Strongyloides*

[1] Nemathelminthes, sometimes used as a synonym for Aschelminthes, only applies to Nematomorpha and Nematoda.
[2] The Priapulida may equally well be considered as a phylum. They have also been grouped with the Echiuroidea, p. 23 and Sipunculoidea, p. 23 as Gephyrea.
[3] Classification by Chitwood & Chitwood (1950) and Thorne (1949).

Sub-order STRONGYLINA

Strongylus (=*Sclerostomum*); *Oesophagostomum* (nodular worm); *Ancylostoma, Necator* (hookworms); *Syngamus* (gape worm); *Haemonchus, Cooperia, Ostertagia* (trichostrongyles); *Metastrongylus, Dictyocaulus, Muellerius* (lungworms)

Sub-order ASCARIDINA

Ascaris (large roundworm); *Parascaris* (horse roundworm); *Ascaridia* (poultry roundworm); *Porrocaecum; Heterakis* (poultry caecal worm); *Subulura; Enterobius* (threadworm, pinworm); *Aspiculuris* (mouse threadworm or pinworm)

Order **TYLENCHIDA**

Ditylenchus (stem-and-bulb eelworm); *Anguina* (wheat gall eelworm); *Heterodera* (cyst eelworm); *Meloidogyne* (root-knot eelworm); *Aphelenchoides* (leaf eelworm); *Sphaerularia*

Order **SPIRURIDA**

Dracunculus (guinea worm); *Wuchereria* (filarial worm); *Loa; Onchocerca; Dirofilaria* (dog heart worm); *Setaria; Thelazia* (eye worm); *Gongylonema* (gullet worm); *Habronema* (horse stomach worm); *Gnathostoma; Philometra; Micropleura; Tetrameres* (=*Tropisurus*) (poultry stomach worm)

Sub-class **APHASMIDIA**

Order **CHROMADORIDA**

Plectus; Monhystera; Paracanthonchus; Cylindrolaimus; Desmoscolex

Order **ENOPLIDA**

Sub-order ENOPLINA

Enoplus; Tripyla; Mononchus

Sub-order DORYLAIMINA

Dorylaimus; Xiphinema; Mermis; Trichuris (=*Trichocephalus*) (whipworm); *Trichinella* (=*Trichina*) (trichina worm); *Capillaria*

Sub-order DIOCTOPHYMATINA

Dioctophyme (dog kidney worm); *Hystrichis*

Phylum **ASCHELMINTHES**

Class **NEMATODA** (roundworms)[1]

Order **ENOPLOIDEA**

Enoplus; Tripyla; Mononchus

Order **DORYLAIMOIDEA**

Dorylaimus; Xiphinema

Order **MERMITHOIDEA**

Mermis

Order **CHROMADOROIDEA**

Paracanthonchus

[1] Alternative classification by Hyman (1951*b*).

Order **ARAEOLAIMOIDEA**
Plectus
Order **MONHYSTEROIDEA**
Cylindrolaimus; Monhystera
Order **DESMOSCOLECOIDEA**
Desmoscolex
Order **RHABDITOIDEA**
(= ANGUILLULOIDEA)
Rhabditis; Diplogaster; Panagrellus (sour paste eel-
worm); *Cephalobus; Turbatrix* (vinegar eelworm);
Heterodera (cyst eelworm); *Ditylenchus* (stem-and-
bulb eelworm); *Anguina* (wheat gall eelworm);
Meloidogyne (root-knot eelworm); *Aphelenchoides*
(leaf eelworm); *Sphaerularia*
Order **RHABDIASOIDEA**
Rhabdias (lung nematode); *Strongyloides*
Order **OXYUROIDEA**
Enterobius (threadworm, pinworm); *Aspiculuris*
(mouse threadworm or pinworm)
Order **ASCAROIDEA**
Ascaris (large roundworm); *Parascaris* (horse
roundworm); *Ascaridia* (poultry roundworm);
Porrocaecum; Heterakis (poultry caecal worm);
Subulura
Order **STRONGYLOIDEA**
Strongylus (= *Sclerostomum*); *Oesophagostomum*
(nodular worm); *Ancylostoma, Necator* (hook-
worms); *Syngamus* (gape worm); *Metastrongylus,
Dictyocaulus, Muellerius* (lungworms);
Haemonchus, Cooperia, Ostertagia (tricho-
strongyles)
Order **SPIRUROIDEA**
Thelazia (eye worm); *Gongylonema* (gullet worm);
Habronema (horse stomach worm); *Gnathostoma;
Tetrameres* (poultry stomach worm)
Order **DRACUNCULOIDEA**
Dracunculus (guinea worm); *Philometra;
Micropleura*
Order **FILARIOIDEA**
Setaria; Wuchereria (filarial worm); *Loa;
Onchocerca; Dirofilaria* (dog heart worm)
Order **TRICHUROIDEA**
(= TRICHINELLOIDEA)
Trichuris (= *Trichocephalus*) (whipworm);
Capillaria; Trichinella (= *Trichina*) (trichina worm)
Order **DIOCTOPHYMOIDEA**
Dioctophyme (dog kidney worm); *Hystrichis*

Phylum **ACANTHOCEPHALA** (thorny-headed worms)

Order **ARCHIACANTHOCEPHALA**
Macracanthorhynchus; Gigantorhynchus; Oncicola;
Moniliformis
Order **PALAEACANTHOCEPHALA**
Polymorphus; Filicollis; Gorgorhynchus;
Echinorhynchus
Order **EOACANTHOCEPHALA**
Quadrigyrus; Neoechinorhynchus; Octospinifer

Phylum **ENTOPROCTA**
(=ENDOPROCTA, CALYSSOZOA, KAMPTOZOA,
POLYZOA ENDOPROCTA, POLYZOA ENTOPROCTA)

Family **LOXOSOMATIDAE**
Loxosoma; Loxocalyx
Family **PEDICELLINIDAE**
Pedicellina; Myosoma; Barentsia
Family **URNATELLIDAE**
Urnatella

Phylum **POLYZOA**
(=BRYOZOA, POLYZOA ECTOPROCTA, ECTOPROCTA)

Class **PHYLACTOLAEMATA**
(=LOPHOPODA)   *Cristatella; Plumatella* (=*Alcyonella*)

Class **GYMNOLAEMATA**
(=STELMATOPODA)   Order **CYCLOSTOMATA**[1]
                                (=STENOLAEMATA, STENOSTOMATA, – TREPOSTOMATA[2])
                                Crisia; Diplosolen; Hornera; Lichenopora;
                                Tubulipora
                                Order **CHEILOSTOMATA**
                                Bugula; Caberea; Cryptosula; Flustra;
(=Eurystomata)   *Membranipora; Schizoporella; Scrupocellaria*
                                Order **CTENOSTOMATA**
                                Alcyonidium; Bowerbankia; Triticella

Phylum **PHORONIDA**

Phoronis; Phoronopsis

[1] See Marsipobranchii, p. 35.
[2] The Trepostomata are extinct.

Phylum BRACHIOPODA

Class INARTICULATA

Order **ATREMATA**
Lingula; Glottidia
Order **NEOTREMATA**
Crania; Discinisca

Class ARTICULATA[1]

Sub-order THECIDEOIDEA
Lacazella
Sub-order RHYNCHONELLOIDEA
Hemithyris; Cryptopora
Sub-order TEREBRATULOIDEA
Gryphus; Terebratulina
Sub-order TEREBRATELLOIDEA
Argyrotheca; Dallina; Terebratella; Magellania

Phylum MOLLUSCA

Class POLYPLACOPHORA[2]
(=LORICATA)

Order **LEPIDOPLEURIDA**
Lepidopleurus
Order **CHITONIDA**
Chiton (coat of mail shell); *Cryptochiton;*
Lepidochiton (=*Lepidochitona*)

Class APLACOPHORA[2]
(=SOLENOGASTRES)

Order **NEOMENIOMORPHA**
Neomenia; Proneomenia
Order **CHAETODERMOMORPHA**
Chaetoderma

Class MONOPLACOPHORA

Order **TRYBLIDIACEA**
Neopilina

Class GASTROPODA

Sub-class PROSOBRANCHIA
(=STREPTONEURA)

Order **ARCHAEOGASTROPODA**
(=DIOTOCARDIA, ASPIDOBRANCHIA)
Acmaea (limpet); *Megathura* (keyhole limpet);
Haliotis (ear-shell, ormer, abalone); *Patella*
(limpet); *Nerita; Pleurotomaria; Trochus* (top-shell)

---

[1] The Articulata (see also Crinoidea, p. 32) used to be divided into two orders, Protremata and Telo-tremata. These overlap and have therefore been discarded. They have not so far been replaced, though the ordinal classification of the Articulata is under review.
[2] These two classes are sometimes grouped together as Amphineura.

Order **MESOGASTROPODA**
(=Monotocardia, Pectinibranchia, −Stenoglossa)
Littorina (periwinkle); *Strombus, Natica* (necklace-shells); *Cypraea* (cowrie); *Carinaria; Viviparus*
(=*Paludina*) (river-snail); *Aporrhais* (pelican's foot-shell); *Crepidula* (slipper limpet); *Charonia*
(=*Tritonia*) (trumpet-shell); *Cassis* (helmet-shell);
Pterotrachea; Bithynia (=*Bulimus*)

Order **STENOGLOSSA**
(=Neogastropoda)
Buccinum (whelk); *Busycon* (=*Sycotypus*)
(American whelk); *Nassa* (=*Ilyanassa*) (dog-whelk); *Murex, Ocenebra* (sting-winkles); *Terebra,
Conus* (arrow-tooth shells)

Sub-class **OPISTHOBRANCHIA**

Order **PLEUROCOELA**
(=Tectibranchia)
Actaeon (actaeon shell); *Aplysia* (sea-hare); *Bulla*
(bubble shell)

Order **PTEROPODA**
Cavolina, Limacina (sea-butterflies); *Clione*

Order **SACOGLOSSA**
(=Ascoglossa)
Elysia, Limapontia (sea-slugs)

Order **ACOELA**[1]
Sub-order Notaspidea
Umbraculum; Pleurobranchus (=*Oscanius*) (sea-slug)
Sub-order Nudibranchia
Onchidoris; Glaucus; Pleurophyllidea; Doris (sea-lemon); *Eolis* (sea-slug)

Sub-class **PULMONATA**

Order **BASOMMATOPHORA**
Lymnaea (=*Limnaea*) (pond snail); *Planorbis*
(ram's horn snail); *Ancylus* (=*Ancylastrum*) (fresh-water limpet)

Order **STYLOMMATOPHORA**
Helix (land snail); *Testacella* (shell-bearing slug);
Limax, Arion (land-slugs)

Class **SCAPHOPODA**

Cadulus, Dentalium, Siphodentalium, Pulsellum
(tusk-shells)

Class **BIVALVIA**
(=Lamellibranchia, Pelecypoda)

Order **PROTOBRANCHIA**
Nucula (nut-shell); *Yoldia; Solenomya*

Order **FILIBRANCHIA**
(=Anisomyaria)
Arca (Noah's ark shell); *Anomia* (saddle-oyster);
Modiolus (horse-mussel); *Mytilus* (mussel); *Pecten*
(scallop)

[1] See Turbellaria, p. 13.

Order **EULAMELLIBRANCHIA**
  Cardium (cockle); *Ostrea* (oyster); *Mya* (gaper);
  Anodonta (= *Anodon*) (swan-mussel); *Unio* (pearl-
  mussel); *Tellina* (tellin); *Pholas* (piddock); *Teredo*
  (ship-worm)
Order **SEPTIBRANCHIA**
  Poromya (gaper); *Cuspidaria*

Class **CEPHALOPODA**
  (= SIPHONOPODA)

Order **TETRABRANCHIA**
  Nautilus (pearly-nautilus)
Order **DIBRANCHIA**
  Sub-order DECAPODA[1]
    Architeuthis; Sepia (= *Eusepia*) (cuttle-fish); *Loligo*
    (squid); *Spirula*
  Sub-order VAMPYROMORPHA
    Vampyroteuthis (vampire squid)
  Sub-order OCTOPODA
    Octopus (= *Polypus*) (octopus); *Argonauta* (paper-
    nautilus); *Eledone* (lesser octopus)

Phylum **SIPUNCULOIDEA**[2]

Golfingia (= *Phascolosoma*)[3]; *Phascolosoma*
(= *Physcosoma, Phymosoma*)[3]; *Sipunculus;*
Dendrostomum; Aspidosiphon; Phascolion

Phylum **ECHIUROIDEA**[2, 4]

Order **ECHIUROINEA**
  Bonellia; Echiurus; Thalassema; Ochetostoma
Order **XENOPNEUSTA**
  Urechis
Order **HETEROMYOTA**
  Ikeda

[1] See Eucarida, p. 31.
[2] The Sipunculoidea and Echiuroidea have also been grouped with the Priapulida, p. 17, as Gephyrea.
[3] *Golfingia* Lankester = *Phascolosoma* (auct.). *Phascolosoma* F. S. Leuckart = *Physcosoma* Selenka, see Fisher (1950).
[4] *Poeobius* is sometimes put in this phylum and sometimes in phylum Poeobioidea. In all probability, however, it is an aberrant polychaete, p. 24.

Phylum **ANNELIDA** (= ANNULATA)

Class **POLYCHAETA**[1]

Amphinome; Aphrodite; Phyllodoce; Tomopteris; Syllis; Nereis; Nephthys; Glycera (= Rhynchobolus); Eunice; Scoloplos; Polydora; Magelona; Chaetopterus; Ophelia; Arenicola (lugworm); *Cirratulus; Capitella; Maldane; Owenia; Pectinaria; Ampharete; Terebella; Sabella (= Spirographis)* (peacock fan worm); *Serpula*

Class **MYZOSTOMARIA**

Myzostoma

Class **OLIGOCHAETA**[2]

Tubifex; Clitellio; Stylaria; Chaetogaster; Enchytraeus (white worm); *Peloscolex; Lumbricus, Pheretima, Allolobophora, Eisenia* (earthworms)

Class **HIRUDINEA** (leeches)

Order **ACANTHOBDELLIDA**
Acanthobdella
Order **RHYNCHOBDELLIDA**
Glossiphonia; Helobdella; Piscicola; Pontobdella; Branchellion
Order **GNATHOBDELLIDA**
Hirudo; Haemopis (= Aulastoma); Macrobdella; Haemadipsa; Erpobdella (= Herpobdella, Nephelis); Trocheta (amphibious leech); *Dina*

Class **ARCHIANNELIDA**

Saccocirrus; Dinophilus; Polygordius; Protodrilus; Nerilla

Phylum **ARTHROPODA**

Class **ONYCHOPHORA**

Peripatus; Peripatopsis

Class **PAUROPODA**

Pauropus

Class **DIPLOPODA** (millipedes)

Sub-class **PSELAPHOGNATHA**

Order **POLYXENIDA**
(= SCHIZOCEPHALA, PENICILLATA)
Polyxenus; Lophoproctus

[1] The Polychaeta, for which no acceptable ordinal classification exists, are sometimes divided for convenience into sub-classes Errantia (the first nine genera) and Sedentaria (the last fifteen genera).
[2] No satisfactory ordinal classification is available for the Oligochaeta, though the first six genera are sometimes assigned to order Limicolae and the last four to order Terricolae.

Sub-class **CHILOGNATHA**
    Super-order **PENTAZONIA**
        (=Opisthandria)
            Order **GLOMERIDA**
                (=Oniscomorpha)
                Glomeris; Sphaerotherium; Castanotherium
            Order **GLOMERIDESMIDA**
                (=Limacomorpha)
                Glomeridesmus
    Super-order **HELMINTHOMORPHA**
        (=Eugnatha, Proterandria)
            Order **NEMATOPHORA**
                (=Chordeumida)
                Chordeuma; Microchordeuma; Callipus
            Order **STEMMIULIDA**
                Stemmatoiulus
            Order **POLYDESMIDA**
                Polydesmus; Oxidus; Platyrrhacus; Orthomorpha
            Order **JULIDA**
                Julus; Blaniulus; Cylindroiulus; Pachyiulus
            Order **SPIROBOLIDA**
                Spirobolus; Trigoniulus; Rhinocricus; Pachybolus
(=Juliformia) Order **SPIROSTREPTIDA**
                Spirostreptus; Odontopyge; Scaphiostreptus;
                Thyropygus
            Order **CAMBALIDA**
                Cambala; Cambalopsis; Cambalomorpha
    Super-order **COLOBOGNATHA**
                Polyzonium; Platydesmus

Class **CHILOPODA** (centipedes)
Sub-class **EPIMORPHA**
            Order **GEOPHILOMORPHA**
                Geophilus; Mecistocephalus; Himantarium; Orya
            Order **SCOLOPENDROMORPHA**
                Scolopendra; Ethmostigmus; Otostigmus; Cryptops
Sub-class **ANAMORPHA**

            Order **HETEROSTIGMATA**
             Sub-order Lithobiomorpha
             Lithobius; Polybothrus; Henicops
             Sub-order Craterostigmomorpha
             Craterostigmus
            Order **SCUTIGEROMORPHA**
             Scutigera

Class **SYMPHYLA**   *Scutigerella; Hanseniella; Symphylella*

Class **INSECTA**
  (=Hexapoda)

Sub-class **APTERYGOTA**
  (=Ametabola)   Order **COLLEMBOLA** (spring-tails)
             Sub-order Arthropleona
             Podura; Orchesella
             Sub-order Symphypleona
             Sminthurus (lucerne flea); *Neelus*

Order **PROTURA**
(= Myrientomata)
Eosentomon; Acerentulus
Order **DIPLURA**
(= Aptera)
Campodea; Japyx
Order **THYSANURA** (bristle-tails)
Machilis; Petrobius; Lepisma (silver fish);
Thermobia (fire brat)

Sub-class **PTERYGOTA**
(= Metabola)
Division Palaeoptera
(= Exopterygota, Hemimetabola, − [Polyneoptera + Paraneoptera])
Order **EPHEMEROPTERA** (may-flies)
(= Plectoptera)
Ephemera; Baetis
Order **ODONATA**
(= Paraneuroptera)
Sub-order Zygoptera   (damsel flies)
Agrion; Coenagrion; Lestes
Sub-order Anisozygoptera
Epiophlebia
Sub-order Anisoptera (true dragonflies)
Aeshna; Anax; Gomphus; Petalura; Cordulegaster; Libellula

Division Neoptera
Section Polyneoptera
(= Exopterygota, Hemimetabola, − [Paraneoptera + Palaeoptera])
Order **DICTYOPTERA**
Sub-order Blattodea (cockroaches)
Blatta; Periplaneta; Blaberus; Ectobius
Sub-order Mantodea (mantids)
Chaetessa; Mantis; Empusa
Order **ISOPTERA** (termites, white ants)
Mastotermes; Kalotermes; Neotermes; Hodotermes
Order **ZORAPTERA**
Zorotypus
Order **PLECOPTERA** (stone-flies)
(= Perlaria)
Eusthenia; Perla; Nemoura
Order **GRYLLOBLATTODEA**
(= Notoptera)
Grylloblatta
Order **PHASMIDA**
(= Cheleutoptera)
Carausius (= *Dixippus*) (stick-insect); *Phyllium*
(leaf-insect)
Order **ORTHOPTERA**
(= Saltatoria)
Sub-order Ensifera (longhorned grasshoppers)
Tettigonia (= *Phasgonura*) (bush cricket);
Gryllotalpa (mole cricket); *Acheta* (= *Gryllus*)
(cricket); *Nemobius; Oecanthus* (snowy cricket)

Sub-order CAELIFERA (shorthorned grasshoppers)

Schistocerca, Locusta (locusts); *Chorthippus* (grass-hopper); *Tetrix* (grouse locust); *Pneumora*

Order **EMBIOPTERA** (web-spinners)

Embia; Oligotoma

Order **DERMAPTERA**

Sub-order FORFICULINA (earwigs)

Labidura; Forficula; Labia

Sub-order ARIXENIINA

Arixenia

Sub-order HEMIMERINA

(=Diploglossata)

Hemimerus

Section PARANEOPTERA

(=Exopterygota, Hemimetabola, – [Polyneoptera + Palaeoptera])

Order **PSOCOPTERA** (book lice)

(=COPEOGNATHA, CORRODENTIA)

Peripsocus; Psocus

Order **PHTHIRAPTERA** (lice)

Sub-order ANOPLURA (sucking lice)

(=Siphunculata)

Pediculus (human louse); *Phthirus* (=*Phthirius*) (crab louse); *Haematopinus* (hog louse); *Linognathus*

Sub-order MALLOPHAGA (biting lice)

Menopon (shaft louse); *Goniodes; Lipeurus* (fowl louse); *Trichodectes*

Sub-order RHYNCHOPHTHIRINA

Haematomyzus (elephant louse)

Order **THYSANOPTERA** (thrips)

(=PHYSOPODA)

Thrips; Heliothrips

Order **HEMIPTERA**

(=RHYNCHOTA)

Sub-order HOMOPTERA

Oiphysa; Magicicada (cicada); *Cercopis, Philaenus* (frog hoppers); *Centrotus* (tree-hopper); *Perkinsiella* (sugar-cane leaf-hopper); *Empoasca* (leaf-hopper); *Phenax* (lantern fly); *Psylla* (jumping plant louse); *Aphis* (greenfly, plant louse); *Phylloxera* (vine pest); *Coccus* (scale insect)

Sub-order HETEROPTERA

Cimex (bed-bug); *Dysdercus* (cotton stainer); *Rhodnius* (assassin bug); *Blissus* (chinch bug); *Notonecta* (backswimmer); *Corixa* (water boat-man)

Section OLIGONEOPTERA

(=Endopterygota, Holometabola)

Order **NEUROPTERA**

Sub-order MEGALOPTERA

Sialis (alder fly); *Raphidia* (snake fly); *Corydalis* (Dobson fly)

Sub-order PLANIPENNIA
Chrysopa (green lacewing); *Hemerobius* (brown lacewing); *Myrmeleon* (ant lion fly); *Ithone; Mantispa*

Order **COLEOPTERA** (beetles)

Sub-order ADEPHAGA
Cicindela (tiger beetle); *Carabus* (ground beetle); *Dytiscus* (water beetle); *Gyrinus* (whirligig)

Sub-order ARCHOSTEMATA
Cupes

Sub-order POLYPHAGA
Hydrophilus (= *Hydrous*); *Hister; Sphaerius; Lucanus* (stag beetle); *Cetonia* (rose chafer); *Stigmodera; Agriotes* (wire worm[1]); *Coccinella* (lady bird); *Tenebrio* (mealworm[1]); *Tribolium* (flour beetle); *Chrysolina; Leptinotarsa* (Colorado beetle); *Dendroctonus*

Order **STREPSIPTERA** (stylopids)
Stylops

Order **MECOPTERA** (scorpion flies)
(= PANORPATAE)
Panorpa; Bittacus; Boreus

Order **TRICHOPTERA** (caddis flies)
(= PHRYGANOIDEA)
Limnephilus

Order **ZEUGLOPTERA**
Micropteryx (= *Eriocephala*)

Order **LEPIDOPTERA**

Sub-order MONOTRYSIA
Eriocrania; Hepialus (ghost moth); *Stigmella; Incurvaria*

Sub-order DITRYSIA
Sitotroga; Depressaria; Cossus (goat moth); *Psyche* (bag-worm moth); *Castnia; Evetria* (pine shoot moth); *Tortrix; Galleria* (wax moth); *Ephestia* (flour moths); *Tinea* (clothes moth); *Attacus* (atlas moth); *Papilio* (swallow-tail); *Pieris* (cabbage butterfly); *Acherontia* (death's head hawk moth); *Lymantria* (gipsy moth); *Bombyx* (silk moth)

Order **DIPTERA** (two-winged flies, true flies)

Sub-order NEMATOCERA
Tipula (daddy-long legs); *Phlebotomus* (sand fly); *Culex, Anopheles* (mosquitoes); *Contarinia* (pear midge); *Sciara* (fungus gnat); *Simulium* (black fly); *Chironomus*

Sub-order BRACHYCERA
Rhagio; Tabanus (horse fly)

Sub-order CYCLORRHAPHA
Eristalis (drone fly); *Drosophila* (small fruit fly); *Oscinella* (frit fly); *Calliphora* (bluebottle, blowfly); *Musca* (house fly); *Lucilia* (greenbottle); *Glossina* (tse-tse fly); *Melophagus* (sheep tick)

[1] Larva.

Order **SIPHONAPTERA** (fleas)
    (=APHANIPTERA, SUCTORIA)
    Xenopsylla; Tunga (jigger); *Pulex;*
    Ctenocephalides; Echidnophaga (sticktight)
Order **HYMENOPTERA**
  Sub-order SYMPHYTA
    (=Chalastogastra)
    Cephus (stem sawfly); *Nematus* (sawfly); *Sirex*
    (giant wood wasp)
  Sub-order APOCRITA
    (=Clistogastra)
    Ichneumon, Nemeritis (ichneumon flies); *Chalcis*
    (chalcid fly); *Blastophaga* (fig-insect);
    Trichogramma; Formica (ant); *Vespa* (hornet);
    Vespula (wasp); *Bombus* (bumble bee); *Apis* (honey
    bee)

Class CRUSTACEA

Sub-class BRANCHIOPODA

Order **ANOSTRACA**
    Chirocephalus; Branchipus; Artemia
Order **NOTOSTRACA**
    Triops (=*Apus*); *Lepidurus*
Order **CONCHOSTRACA**
    Cyzicus (=*Estheria*); *Limnadia*
Order **CLADOCERA** (water fleas)
    Sida; Daphnia; Simocephalus; Moina; Leptodora;
    Podon; Evadne
Order **CEPHALOCARIDA**
    Hutchinsoniella

Sub-class OSTRACODA

Order **MYODOCOPA**
    Cypridina; Pyrocypris
Order **CLADOCOPA**
    Polycope
Order **PODOCOPA**
    Cypris; Cythere; Candona
Order **PLATYCOPA**
    Cytherella

Sub-class COPEPODA

Order **CALANOIDA**
    Calanus; Diaptomus
Order **MONSTRILLOIDA**
    Monstrilla
Order **CYCLOPOIDA**
    Cyclops; Lernaea (=*Lernaeocera*)[1]
Order **HARPACTICOIDA**
    Tigriopus; Harpacticus
Order **NOTODELPHYOIDA**
    Ascidicola
Order **CALIGOIDA**
    Caligus; Lernaeocera (=*Lernaea*)[1]

---

[1] *Lernaeocera* is the *Lernaea* of textbooks and classrooms. The fresh-water genus *Lernaea* used to be called *Lernaeocera* (Gurney, 1933, p. 336).

Order **LERNAEOPODOIDA**
Chondracanthus; Sphaeronella

Sub-class **MYSTACOCARIDA**

Order **DEROCHEILOCARIDA**
Derocheilocaris

Sub-class **BRANCHIURA**   *Argulus; Dolops*

Sub-class **CIRRIPEDIA**

Order **THORACICA** (barnacles)
Lepas (goose barnacle); *Balanus; Chthamalus; Elminius*
Order **ACROTHORACICA**
Alcippe
Order **RHIZOCEPHALA**
Sacculina
Order **ASCOTHORACICA**
Laura

Sub-class **MALACOSTRACA**
Super-order **LEPTOSTRACA**
(=PHYLLOCARIDA)
Order **NEBALIACEA**
Nebalia
Super-order **SYNCARIDA**
Order **ANASPIDACEA**
Anaspides
Order **BATHYNELLACEA**
Bathynella
Super-order **PERACARIDA**
Order **MYSIDACEA** (opossum-shrimps)
Lophogaster; Gnathophausia; Mysis; Hemimysis; Siriella; Gastrosaccus
Order **CUMACEA**
Diastylis; Iphinoe; Pseudocuma
Order **TANAIDACEA**
Apseudes; Tanais; Leptochelia; Syraphus
Order **GNATHIIDEA**
Gnathia
Order **ISOPODA**
Ligia, Armadillidium (woodlice); *Asellus; Idotea; Limnoria* (gribble); *Bopyrus; Ione; Cymothoa; Portunion; Entoniscus*
Order **SPELAEOGRIPHACEA**
Spelaeogriphus
Order **AMPHIPODA**
Gammarus (fresh-water shrimp); *Talitrus* (shore hopper); *Caprella* (ghost shrimp); *Hyperia; Cyamus* (whale louse); *Corophium; Jassa*
Super-order **HOPLOCARIDA**
Order **STOMATOPODA** (mantis shrimps)
Squilla; Gonodactylus
Super-order **PANCARIDA**
Order **THERMOSBAENACEA**
Thermosbaena; Monodella
Super-order **EUCARIDA**
Order **EUPHAUSIACEA** (krill, whale feed)
Euphausia;   *hanes*

Order **DECAPODA**[1]

Sub-order NATANTIA

Penaeus, Pandalus, Palaemon (*=Leander*) (prawns);
Crangon (*=Crago*), *Hippolyte* (shrimps);
Macrobrachium (*=Palaemon*) (river prawn)

Sub-order REPTANTIA

Cambarus, Astacus (*=Potamobius*) (fresh-water crayfish); *Homarus* (lobster); *Nephrops* (Norway lobster); *Jasus* (kreef); *Palinurus* (langouste, crawfish); *Panulirus* (rock lobster); *Cancer* (edible crab); *Pagurus* (*=Eupagurus*), *Dardanus* (*=Pagurus*) (hermit crabs); *Lithodes* (stone crab); *Carcinus* (shore crab); *Maia* (spider crab); *Callinectes* (blue crab); *Potamon* (*=Telphusa*) (river crab); *Uca* (fiddler crab)

Class **MEROSTOMATA**[2]

Order **XIPHOSURA** (king crabs)
  (*=*LIMULIDA)
Limulus; Tachypleus

Class **ARACHNIDA**[2]

Order **SCORPIONES** (scorpions)
Scorpio; Apistobuthus; Buthus; Tityus; Pandinus

Order **PSEUDOSCORPIONES** (false scorpions)
  (*=*CHELONETHI, CHERNETES)
Microbisium; Chelifer; Garypus; Chthonius

(*=*Pedipalpi)

Order **UROPYGI** (whip scorpions)
  (*=*THELYPHONIDA, SCHIZOMIDA, TARTARIDAE)
Mastigoproctus; Schizomus

Order **AMBLYPYGI**
  (*=*PHRYNICIDA)
Damon; Phrynichus; Charinus

Order **PALPIGRADI** (micro-whip scorpions)
  (*=*MICROTHELYPHONIDA)
Koenenia

Order **RICINULEI**
  (*=*PODOGONATA)
Ricinoides

Order **SOLIFUGAE** (false spiders, sun spiders, wind scorpions)
  (*=*SOLPUGIDA)
Galeodes

Order **OPILIONES** (phalangids, harvest spiders, harvestmen)
  (*=*PHALANGIDA)
Phalangium; Oligolophus

Order **ARANEAE** (spiders)
Araneus; (*=Epeira*); *Atrax; Latrodectus; Pholcus*

Order **ACARI**
Acarus, Dermanyssus, Pyemotes, Trombicula (mites); *Ixodes, Argas, Ornithodoros* (ticks)

Class **PYCNOGONIDA**[2] (sea spiders)
  (*=*PANTOPODA)

Order **COLOSSENDEOMORPHA**
Dodecolopoda; Colossendeis

[1] See also Dibranchia, p. 23.
[2] These three classes may be considered as members of sub-phylum Chelicerata.

Order **NYMPHONOMORPHA**
Nymphon
Order **ASCORHYNCHOMORPHA**
Ascorhynchus
Order **PYCNOGONOMORPHA**
Pycnogonum

Class **PENTASTOMIDA**

Order **CEPHALOBAENIDA**
Cephalobaena; Reighardia
Order **POROCEPHALIDA**
Sebekia; Linguatula

Class **TARDIGRADA** (water-bears)

Order **HETEROTARDIGRADA**
Echiniscus; Tetrakentron
Order **EUTARDIGRADA**
Macrobiotus; Hypsibius; Milnesium

Phylum **CHAETOGNATHA** (arrow worms)

Sagitta; Spadella; Eukrohnia; Pterosagitta;
Heterokrohnia

Phylum **POGONOPHORA** (=Brachiata) (beard worms)

Order **ATHECANEPHRIA**
Oligobrachia; Siboglinum
Order **THECANEPHRIA**
Heptabrachia; Zenkevitchiana; Lamellisabella;
Spirobrachia

Phylum **ECHINODERMATA**

Sub-phylum **PELMATOZOA**

Class **CRINOIDEA**

Order **ARTICULATA**[1]
Antedon, Tropiometra (feather stars); *Rhizocrinus,*
Metacrinus (sea lilies)

Sub-phylum **ELEUTHEROZOA**

Class **HOLOTHUROIDEA** (sea cucumbers)

Order **ASPIDOCHIROTA**
Holothuria; Stichopus; Mesothuria
Order **ELASIPODA**
Deima; Kolga; Elpidia; Pelagothuria

[1] See Brachiopoda, p. 21.

Order **DENDROCHIROTA**
Cucumaria; Thyone; Echinocucumis; Psolus;
Phyllophorus
Order **MOLPADONIA**
Molpadia
Order **APODA**[1]
Synapta; Leptosynapta; Labidoplax

Class **ECHINOIDEA**

Sub-class **PERIS CHOECHINOIDEA**
Order **CIDAROIDA** (sea urchins)
Cidaris
Sub-class **EUECHINOIDEA**
Super-order **DIADEMATACEA** (sea urchins)
Order **DIADEMATOIDA**
Diadema; Centrostephanus
Order **ECHINOTHURIOIDA**
Phormosoma; Areosoma
Super-order **ECHINACEA** (sea urchins)
Order **HEMICIDAROIDA**
Salenia
Order **PHYMOSOMATOIDA**
Stomopneustes
Order **ARBACIOIDA**
Arbacia
Order **TEMNOPLEUROIDA**
Temnopleurus; Tripneustes (=Hipponoè);
Toxopneustes; Mespilia; Sphaerechinus; Lytechinus;
Pseudocentrotus
Order **ECHINOIDA**
Echinus; Echinometra; Strongylocentrotus;
Psammechinus; Paracentrotus; Hemicentrotus;
Anthocidaris; Heliocidaris
Super-order **GNATHOSTOMATA**
Order **HOLECTYPOIDA**
Sub-order ECHINONEINA
Echinoneus
Order **CLYPEASTEROIDA** (sand-dollars, cake
urchins)
Sub-order CLYPEASTERINA
Clypeaster
Sub-order LAGANINA
Laganum; Echinocyamus
Sub-order SCUTELLINA
Mellita; Echinarachnius; Dendraster
Sub-order ROTULINA
Rotula
Super-order **ATELOSTOMATA**
Order **NUCLEOLITOIDA**
Neolampas
Order **CASSIDULOIDA**
Cassidulus

[1] See Gymnophiona, p. 41.

Order **HOLASTEROIDA**
Pourtalesia
Order **SPATANGOIDA** (heart urchins)
Spatangus; Echinocardium; Brissopsis

Class **ASTEROIDEA** (starfishes)

Order **PHANEROZONA**
Astropecten; Porcellanaster; Luidia
Order **SPINULOSA**
*Asterina; Patiria; Anseropoda (=Palmipes);
Henricia; Solaster*
Order **FORCIPULATA**
*Marthasterias; Asterias; Leptasterias;
Stichastrella; Pisaster; Brisinga*

Class **OPHIUROIDEA** (brittle stars)

Order **OPHIURAE** (serpent stars)
*Ophiura; Ophiothrix; Ophiocomina; Ophiopsila;
Ophiactis; Ophiopholis; Acrocnida; Amphiura;
Amphipholis*
Order **EURYALAE**
Asteronyx; Gorgonocephalus

Phylum CHORDATA

Sub-phylum HEMICHORDATA
(=STOMOCHORDATA, BRANCHIOTREMATA)

Class **ENTEROPNEUSTA** (acorn worms)

*Protoglossus (=Protobalanus); Saccoglossus
(=Dolichoglossus); Harrimania; Glossobalanus;
Balanoglossus; Ptychodera; Schizocardium;
Glandiceps*

Class **PTEROBRANCHIA**

Order **RHABDOPLEURIDA**
Rhabdopleura
Order **CEPHALODISCIDA**
Cephalodiscus; Atubaria

Class **PLANCTOSPHAEROIDEA**[1]

Planctosphaera

Sub-phylum UROCHORDATA (=TUNICATA)

Class **ASCIDIACEA** (sea squirts)

Order **ENTEROGONA**
Sub-order APLOUSOBRANCHIATA
*Clavelina; Polyclinum; Aplidium (=Amaroucium);
Didemnum*
Sub-order PHLEBOBRANCHIATA
Ciona; Ascidia; Phallusia; Ascidiella; Perophora

[1] This class only contains a few larvae of unknown parentage.

Order **PLEUROGONA**
Sub-order STOLIDOBRANCHIATA
Styela; Polycarpa; Botryllus; Boltenia; Pyura;
Molgula
Sub-order ASPIRICULATA
Hexacrobylus

Class **THALIACEA**

Order **PYROSOMIDA**
Pyrosoma
Order **DOLIOLIDA**
(=CYCLOMYARIA)
Doliolum
Order **SALPIDA**
(=DESMOMYARIA)
Salpa

Class **LARVACEA**

Order **COPELATA**
Oikopleura; Appendicularia; Fritillaria

Sub-phylum **CEPHALOCHORDATA** (=ACRANIA, LEPTOCARDII)

Branchiostoma (=*Amphioxus*) (lancelet);
Asymmetron

Sub-phylum **VERTEBRATA**

Class **MARSIPOBRANCHII**
(=AGNATHA)

Sub-class **CYCLOSTOMATA**[1]

Order **HYPEROARTII** (lampreys)
(=PETROMYZONES)
Petromyzon; Lampetra; Ichthyomyzon
Order **HYPEROTRETI** (hagfishes)
(=MYXINI)
Heptatretus (=*Bdellostoma*); *Myxine*

Class **SELACHII**
(=CHONDROPTERYGII, CHONDRICHTHYES, ELASMOBRANCHII)

Sub-class **EUSELACHII**

Order **PLEUROTREMATA** (sharks, dogfishes, angel-fishes)
(=SELACHOIDEI)
Sub-order NOTIDANOIDEA
(=Hexanchiformes)
Heptranchias; Notidanus

[1] See Gymnolaemata, p. 20.

Sub-order GALEOIDEA
  (=Lamniformes)
  Orectolobus; Odontaspis (=*Carcharias*);
  Scyliorhinus (=*Scyllium*) (dogfish); *Mustelus;*
  Galeorhinus (=*Galeus, Eugaleus*) (tope); *Sphyrna*
  (hammerhead); *Carcharhinus*
Sub-order SQUALOIDEA
  (=Tectospondyli)
  Squalus (=*Acanthias*); *Echinorhinus; Heterodontus*
  (=*Cestracion*); *Pristiophorus; Squatina* (angel-fish)
Order HYPOTREMATA (rays)
Sub-order NARCOBATOIDEA
  (=Torpediniformes)
  Torpedo (=*Narcobatus, Narcacion*)
Sub-order BATOIDEA
  Raja (ray); *Pristis* (saw-fish); *Dasyatis* (=*Trygon*)
  (sting ray)

Class BRADYODONTI

Sub-class HOLOCEPHALI (rabbit-fishes)
  Rhinochimaera; Callorhinchus; Chimaera; Harriotta

Class PISCES (bony fishes)
  (=OSTEICHTHYES)

Sub-class PALAEOPTERYGII

Order CHONDROSTEI
  (=ACIPENSERIFORMES)
  Acipenser (sturgeon); *Polyodon* (paddle-fish)
Order CLADISTIA
  (=POLYPTERIFORMES)
  Polypterus (bichir); *Calamoichthys*
  (=*Erpetoichthys*) (reed-fish)

Sub-class NEOPTERYGII
  (≑ TELEOSTEI + HOLOSTEI)[1]

(=Holostei){
  Order PROTOSPONDYLI (bow-fins)
    Amia
  Order GINGLYMODI (gar-pikes)
    (=LEPISOSTEIFORMES)
    Lepisosteus (=*Lepidosteus*)
Order ISOSPONDYLI
  (=MALACOPTERYGII, CLUPEIFORMES)
Sub-order CLUPEOIDEA
  Clupea (herring); *Sardina* (sardine, pilchard);
  Megalops (tarpon); *Alepocephalus*
Sub-order STOMIATOIDEA
  Stomias
Sub-order SALMONOIDEA
  Salmo (=*Trutta*) (salmon, trout); *Salvelinus* (char);
  Osmerus (smelt)
Sub-order OSTEOGLOSSOIDEA
  Arapaima

[1] i.e., Teleostei ≑ Neopterygii−Holostei.

Sub-order NOTOPTEROIDEA
Notopterus
Sub-order MORMYROIDEA
Gymnarchus
Sub-order GONORHYNCHOIDEA
Gonorhynchus
Order **HAPLOMI**
(=ESOCOIDEI)
Esox (pike); *Dallia* (black-fish); *Umbra* (mud-minnow)
Order **INIOMI**
(=SCOPELIFORMES)
Sub-order MYCTOPHOIDEA
(=Scopelidae)
Myctophum, Lampanyctus (lantern-fishes); *Synodus* (lizard-fish)
Sub-order ALEPISAUROIDEA
Alepisaurus; Paralepis
Order **CHONDROBRACHII**
Ateleopus
Order **CETUNCULI**
Cetomimus (=*Pelecinomimus*)
Order **MIRIPINNATI**
Eutaeniophorus
Order **GIGANTUROIDEA**
Gigantura
Order **LYOMERI** (gulper eels)
(=SACCOPHARYNGIFORMES)
Saccopharynx; Eurypharynx
Order **OSTARIOPHYSI**
Sub-order CYPRINOIDEA
(=Eventognathi)
Copeina; Electrophorus (electric eel); *Rutilus* (roach); *Phoxinus* (=*Phonixus*) (minnow); *Cyprinus* (carp)
Sub-order SILUROIDEA (catfishes)
(=Nematognathi)
Silurus; Diplomystes; Malapterurus (electric cat-fish)
Order **HETEROMI**
(=NOTACANTHIFORMES)
Halosaurus; Notacanthus
Order **APODES** (eels)
(=ANGUILLIFORMES)
Anguilla; Conger; Muraena (moray)
Order **SYNENTOGNATHI**
(=SCOMBRESOCES, BELONIFORMES)
Sub-order SCOMBRESOCOIDEA
Scombresox (skipper); *Belone* (garfish)
Sub-order EXOCOETOIDEA
Exocoetus (flying fish)
Order **SALMOPERCAE**
(=PERCOPSIFORMES)
Aphredoderus (pirate-perch); *Percopsis* (sand-roller)

Order **MICROCYPRINI**
    (=CYPRINODONTES, CYPRINODONTIFORMES)
Fundulus (killifish); *Oryzias* (medaka, killifish);
Lebistes (guppy); *Platypoecilus* (platyfish, sword-
tail); *Anableps* (four-eyed fish)

Order **SOLENICHTHYES**
    (=SYNGNATHIFORMES +AULOSTOMIFORMES)
Macrorhamphosus (snipe-fish); *Hippocampus* (sea-
horse)

Order **ANACANTHINI**
    (=GADIFORMES + MACRURIFORMES)
Gadus (cod, whiting); *Merluccius* (hake);
Macrourus

Order **ALLOTRIOGNATHI**
    (=LAMPRIDIFORMES)
Lampris (moon-fish); *Trachypterus* (ribbon-fish)

Order **BERYCOMORPHI**
Beryx; Monocentris

Order **ZEOMORPHI**
Zeus (John Dory); *Capros* (boar-fish)

Order **PERCOMORPHI**[1]
Sub-order PERCOIDEA
Perca (perch); *Morone* (bass)
Sub-order TEUTHIDOIDEA
    (=Siganoidei)
Teuthis
Sub-order ACANTHUROIDEA
Acanthurus (surgeon-fish)
Sub-order KURTOIDEA
Kurtus
Sub-order TRICHIUROIDEA
Lepidopus (frost fish); *Aphanopus* (scabbard fish)
Sub-order SCOMBROIDEA
Scomber (mackerel); *Thunnus* (tunny)
Sub-order GOBIOIDEA
Gobius (goby); *Periophthalmus* (mud-skipper)
Sub-order CALLIONYMOIDEA (dragonets)
Callionymus
Sub-order BLENNIOIDEA
Blennius (blenny); *Anarhichas* (sea catfish, wolf-
fish)
Sub-order OPHIDIOIDEA (cusk eels)
Genypterus
Sub-order STROMATEOIDEA
Lirus (rudder-fish); *Nomeus*
Sub-order CHANNOIDEA
    (=Ophicephaloidea)
Channa (=*Ophicephalus*)
Sub-order ANABANTOIDEA
Anabas (climbing perch)
Sub-order MUGILOIDEA (grey mullets)
    (=Percesoces)
Mugil; Atherina; Sphyraena (barracuda)

[1] Acanthopterygii which, *inter alia*, includes the Percomorphi, is obsolete.

Sub-order POLYNEMOIDEA
    (=Rhegnopteri)
Polynemus
Order **SCLEROPAREI** (mail-cheeked fishes)
    (=CATAPHRACTI, LORICATI)
Sub-order SCORPAENOIDEA
    Sebastes; Trigla (gurnard); *Cottus* (bullhead, miller's thumb)
Sub-order CEPHALACANTHOIDEA (flying gurnards)
    (=Dactylopteroidea)
Cephalacanthus (=*Dactylopterus*)
Order **THORACOSTEI** (sticklebacks)
    (=GASTEROSTOIDEA)
Gasterosteus; Spinachia
Order **HYPOSTOMIDES** (dragon-fishes)
    (=PEGASIFORMES)
Pegasus
Order **HETEROSOMATA** (flat-fishes)
    (=PLEURONECTIFORMES)
Bothus; Pleuronectes; Psettodes; Limanda (flounder); *Solea*
Order **DISCOCEPHALI** (sucker-fishes)
    (=ECHENEIFORMES)
Echeneis; Remora
Order **PLECTOGNATHI** (trigger-fishes, globe-fishes)
    ($\doteqdot$ TETRAODONTIFORMES)
Sub-order BALISTOIDEA
    (=Sclerodermi)
Balistes
Sub-order TETRAODONTOIDEA
    (=Gymnodontes)
Tetraodon (puffer); *Mola* (=*Orthagoriscus*) (sun-fish)
Order **MALACICHTHYES** (rag-fishes)
    (=ICOSTEIFORMES)
Icosteus; Acrotus
Order **XENOPTERYGII** (Cornish suckers, cling-fishes)
    (=GOBIESOCIFORMES)
Lepadogaster
Order **HAPLODOCI** (toad-fishes)
    (=BATRACHOIDIFORMES)
Opsanus; Thalassophryne
Order **PEDICULATI**
    (=LOPHIIFORMES)
Sub-order LOPHIOIDEA
Lophius (angler)
Sub-order ANTENNARIOIDEA (sea toads, frog fishes)
Pterophryne; Antennarius
Sub-order CERATIOIDEA (deep-sea anglerfishes)
Melanocetus
Order **OPISTHOMI** (spiny eels)
    (=MASTACEMBELIFORMES)
Mastacembelus; Macrognathus (=*Rhynchobdella*)

Order **SYNBRANCHII**
Sub-order ALABETOIDEA
Alabes (shore eel)
Sub-order SYNBRANCHOIDEA
Synbranchus; Amphipnous

Sub-class **CROSSOPTERYGII**

Order **ACTINISTIA**
(= COELACANTHINI)
Latimeria (coelacanth)
Order **DIPNOI** (lung-fishes)
(= DIPNEUSTI, CERATODIFORMES)
Protopterus; Lepidosiren; Neoceratodus
(= *Ceratodus*)

Class **AMPHIBIA**

Order **CAUDATA**
(= URODELA)
Sub-order CRYPTOBRANCHOIDEA
Hynobius; Pachypalaminus; Megalobatrachus (giant salamander); *Cryptobranchus* (hellbender)
Sub-order AMBYSTOMOIDEA
Ambystoma (= *Amblystoma*) (mole salamander, 'axolotl'[1]); *Siredon* (axolotl); *Dicamptodon* (Pacific giant salamander); *Rhyacotriton* (olympic salamander)
Sub-order SALAMANDROIDEA
Salamandra (fire salamander, etc.); *Triturus* (= *Triton*) (newt); *Diemictylus* (eastern newt); *Desmognathus* (dusky salamander); *Plethodon* (woodland salamander); *Pleurodeles* (pleurodele newt); *Amphiuma* (Congo eel)
Sub-order PROTEIDA
Proteus (olm); *Necturus* (mud-puppy, waterdog)
Sub-order MEANTES
Siren (siren, mud-eel); *Pseudobranchus* (dwarf siren)
Order **SALIENTIA**
(= ANURA)
Sub-order AMPHICOELA
Leiopelma (= *Liopelma*) (New Zealand frog); *Ascaphus* (tailed frog)
Sub-order OPISTHOCOELA
Discoglossus (painted frog); *Alytes* (midwife toad); *Bombina* (= *Bombinator*) (fire bellied toad); *Xenopus* (clawed toad); *Pipa* (Surinam toad)
Sub-order ANOMOCOELA
Megophrys (bull toad); *Pelobates* (European spade foot)
Sub-order PROCOELA
Bufo (toad, true toad); *Hyla* (tree frog); *Gastrotheca* (= *Nototrema*) (marsupial frog); *Eleutherodactylus* (= *Hylodes*) (robber frog); *Rhinophrynus* (Mexican digger toad); *Dendrobates* (poison frog)

[1] Some three years ago the late Dr. Karl P. Schmidt proposed to the Commission on Zoological Nomenclature that the name *Siredon* should be suppressed. He saw no reason to believe that the axolotl, *Siredon mexicanum*, belonged to a different genus from *Ambystoma*. Until the Commission reaches a decision, the axolotl is *Siredon mexicanum*, while mole salamanders are species of *Ambystoma*.

Sub-order DIPLASIOCOELA
Rana (frog, true frog); *Astylosternus* (hairy frog);
Rhacophorus (= *Polypedates*) (tree frog); *Microhyla*,
Callulina

Order **GYMNOPHIONA** (caecilians)
(= APODA[1])
*Caecilia; Scolecomorphus; Hypogeophis;
Ichthyophis; Gymnopis*

Class **REPTILIA** (reptiles)

Order **RHYNCHOCEPHALIA**
Sphenodon (= *Hatteria*) (tuatara)

Order **TESTUDINES**
(= CHELONIA)
Sub-order CRYPTODIRA
Testudo (Greek tortoise, etc.); *Chelone* (green
turtle); *Dermochelys* (leathery turtle); *Chrysemys*
(terrapin); *Trionyx* (soft-shelled turtle)
Sub-order PLEURODIRA
Chelus (matamata); *Chelodina* (long necked turtle)

Order **CROCODYLIA**
(= LORICATA)
Crocodylus[2] (crocodile); *Gavialis* (Indian 'gharial');
Tomistoma (Malayan gavial); *Caiman* (South
American caiman); *Alligator* (alligator)

Order **SQUAMATA**
Sub-order SAURIA (lizards)
(= Lacertilia)
Hemidactylus (gecko); *Iguana* (iguana); *Anguis*
(slow-worm); *Heloderma* (Gila monster); *Lacerta*
(green lizard, wall lizard, etc.); *Chamaeleo*
(chamaeleon)
Sub-order SERPENTES (snakes)
(= Ophidia)
Constrictor (boa); *Python* (python); *Natrix*
(= *Tropidonotus*) (grass snake, water snake, etc.);
Naja (cobra); *Vipera* (= *Pelias*) (viper, adder);
Crotalus (rattle snake)

Class **AVES** (birds)

Order **STRUTHIONIFORMES** (ostriches)
Struthio

Order **RHEIFORMES** (rheas)
Rhea

Order **CASUARIIFORMES**
Dromiceius (emu); *Casuarius* (cassowary)

Order **APTERYGIFORMES** (kiwis)
Apteryx

Order **TINAMIFORMES** (tinamous)
(= CRYPTURI)
Rhynchotus; Crypturellus; Nothura; Nothoprocta

[1] See Holothuroidea, p. 33.
[2] This is the original and, therefore, correct spelling, by Laurenti in 1768.

Order **GAVIIFORMES** (divers)
  (=Pygopodes, Colymbiformes)
  Gavia (=*Colymbus*)
Order **PODICIPEDIFORMES** (grebes)
  (=Pygopodes, Colymbiformes)
  Podiceps; Aechmophorus; Podilymbus
Order **SPHENISCIFORMES** (penguins)
  Spheniscus; Aptenodytes; Eudyptes
Order **PROCELLARIIFORMES**
  (=Tubinares)
  Hydrobates (storm petrel); *Procellaria* (shear-
  water);[1] *Diomedea* (albatross); *Pelecanoides* (diving
  petrel)
Order **PELECANIFORMES**
  (=Steganopodes)
  Phaethon (tropic bird); *Pelecanus* (pelican);
  Phalacrocorax (cormorant); *Sula* (gannet); *Fregata*
  (frigate bird)
Order **CICONIIFORMES**
  (=Ardeiformes, Gressores)
  Ardea (heron); *Balaeniceps* (whale-headed stork);
  Ciconia (stork); *Threskiornis* (ibis); *Scopus*
  (hammerhead); *Platalea* (spoonbill)
Order **PHOENICOPTERIFORMES** (flamingos)
  Phoenicopterus
Order **ANSERIFORMES**
  Anhima (screamer); *Anas* (duck); *Anser* (goose);
  Cygnus (swan)
Order **FALCONIFORMES**
  (=Accipitres)
  Cathartes (turkey vulture); *Sagittarius* (secretary
  bird); *Aegypius* (black vulture); *Accipiter* (=*Astur*)
  (goshawk, sparrow hawk); *Falco* (=*Cerchneis*)
  (kestrel, falcon, etc.); *Pandion* (osprey)
Order **GALLIFORMES**
  Crax (curassow); *Megapodius* (megapode);
  Phasianus (pheasant); *Gallus* (fowl); *Numida*
  (guinea fowl); *Meleagris* (turkey); *Opisthocomus*
  (hoatzin)
Order **GRUIFORMES**
  Mesoenas (roatelo); *Turnix* (button-quail); *Grus*
  (crane); *Aramus* (limpkin); *Psophia* (trumpeter);
  Rallus (rail); *Heliornis* (sun-grebe); *Rhynochetos*
  (kagu); *Eurypyga* (sun-bittern); *Cariama* (cariama);
  Otis (bustard)
Order **CHARADRIIFORMES**
  (=Laro-Limicolae)
  Jacana (lily trotter); *Charadrius* (ringed plover,
  sand plover, etc.); *Stercorarius* (=*Lestris*) (skua);
  Larus (gull); *Sterna* (tern); *Alca* (razorbill);
  Fratercula (puffin)

---

[1] The correct Latin name of the Manx shearwater (formerly *Puffinus puffinus*) is *Procellaria puffinus*.

Order **COLUMBIFORMES**
> *Treron* (green pigeon); *Columba* (pigeon); *Goura* (crowned pigeon); *Pterocles* (sand-grouse)

Order **PSITTACIFORMES** (parrots)
> *Psittacus; Nestor; Eos; Poicephalus; Agapornis; Melopsittacus* (budgerigar)

Order **CUCULIFORMES**
> *Cuculus* (cuckoo); *Crotophaga* (ani); *Geococcyx* (road-runner); *Centropus* (coucal); *Musophaga* (plantain-eater)

Order **STRIGIFORMES** (owls)
> *Tyto; Bubo*

Order **CAPRIMULGIFORMES**
> *Steatornis* (oil bird); *Podargus* (frogmouth); *Caprimulgus* (nightjar)

Order **APODIFORMES**
> (=MICROPODIFORMES, MACROCHIRES)
> *Apus* (=*Micropus*) (swift); *Trochilus* (humming-bird)

Order **COLIIFORMES** (mouse birds)
> *Colius*

Order **TROGONIFORMES** (trogons)
> *Pharomachrus* (quetzal); *Apaloderma*

Order **CORACIIFORMES**
> *Alcedo* (kingfisher); *Todus* (tody); *Momotus* (motmot); *Merops* (bee-eater); *Coracias* (roller); *Upupa* (hoopoe); *Buceros* (horn-bill)

Order **PICIFORMES**
> *Bucco* (puffbird); *Galbula* (jacamar); *Capito* (barbet); *Indicator* (honey guide); *Ramphastos* (toucan); *Picus* (woodpecker)

Order **PASSERIFORMES**
> Sub-order EURYLAIMI (broadbills)
> *Smithornis*
> Sub-order TYRANNI
> *Formicarius* (antbird); *Furnarius* (ovenbird); *Cotinga* (cotinga)
> Sub-order MENURAE
> *Menura* (lyre-bird)
> Sub-order PASSERES (songbirds)
> (=Oscines)
> *Alauda* (lark); *Hirundo* (swallow); *Turdus* (thrush, blackbird); *Fringilla* (chaffinch, etc.); *Sturnus* (starling); *Corvus* (raven, crow, etc.)

Class **MAMMALIA**

Sub-class **PROTOTHERIA**

Order **MONOTREMATA**
> *Tachyglossus* (=*Echidna*) (spiny anteater); *Ornithorhynchus* (=*Platypus*) (duck-bill)

Sub-class **THERIA**

Infra-class **METATHERIA**

Order **MARSUPIALIA**

Didelphis (American opossum); *Antechinomys* (jerboa pouched mouse); *Dasyurus* ('native cat'); *Perameles* (bandicoot); *Trichosurus* (common phalanger); *Vombatus* (=*Phascolomis*) (wombat); *Phascolarctos* (koala); *Macropus, Bettongia* (kangaroos); *Setonyx* (quokka); *Potorous* (rat-kangaroo)

Infra-class **EUTHERIA**

Order **INSECTIVORA**

Tenrec (=*Centetes*) (tenrec); *Erinaceus* (hedgehog); *Echinosorex* (=*Gymnura*) (moon rat); *Sorex* (shrew); *Crocidura* (white-toothed shrew); *Scalopus* (eastern mole); *Talpa* (common old world mole); *Chrysochloris* (golden mole); *Macroscelides* (elephant shrew)

Order **DERMOPTERA**

Cynocephalus (=*Galeopithecus, Galeopterus*) (flying lemur, cobego, colugo)

Order **CHIROPTERA**

Sub-order MEGACHIROPTERA

Pteropus (flying fox); *Cynopterus, Epomophorus* (fruit bats)

Sub-order MICROCHIROPTERA

Rhinolophus (horseshoe bat); *Pipistrellus* (pipistrelle); *Myotis* (brown bat, etc.); *Desmodus* (vampire)

Order **PRIMATES**

Sub-order PROSIMII

(=Lemuroidea)

Tupaia (tree shrew); *Loris* (loris); *Perodicticus* (potto); *Galago* (bush baby); *Lemur* (common lemur)

Sub-order TARSII

Tarsius (tarsier)

Sub-order SIMIAE

(=Anthropoidea)

Hapale (=*Callithrix*) (marmoset); *Cebus* (capuchin); *Saimiri* (squirrel monkey); *Ateles* (spider monkey); *Macaca* (macaque); *Cercocebus* (mangabey); *Papio* (baboon); *Cercopithecus* (African tree monkeys); *Presbytis* (langur); *Hylobates* (gibbon); *Pongo* (=*Simia*) (orang); *Pan* (=*Anthropopithecus, Troglodytes*) (chimpanzee); *Gorilla* (gorilla); *Homo* (man)

Order **EDENTATA**

Bradypus (three-toed sloth); *Dasypus* (armadillo); *Priodontes* (giant armadillo); *Myrmecophaga* (giant anteater); *Tamandua* (lesser anteater)

Order **PHOLIDOTA**

Manis (pangolin, scaly anteater)

Order **LAGOMORPHA**

Ochotona (pika); *Lepus* (hare); *Oryctolagus*
(=*Lepus*) (rabbit); *Sylvilagus* (cottontail)

Order **RODENTIA**

Sub-order Sᴄɪᴜʀᴏᴍᴏʀᴘʜᴀ

Sciurus (squirrel); *Marmota* (=*Arctomys*) (marmot, woodchuck); *Tamias* (chipmunk); *Castor*
(beaver); *Aplodontia* (sewellel, mountain beaver);
Xerus (African ground squirrel); *Citellus* (=*Sperm-
ophilus*) (American ground squirrel, gopher);
Glaucomys (American flying squirrel); *Geomys*
(pocket gopher); *Anomalurus* (scale-tailed flying
squirrel)

Sub-order Mʏᴏᴍᴏʀᴘʜᴀ

Peromyscus (deer mouse); *Sigmodon* (cotton rat);
Cricetus (hamster); *Mesocricetus* (golden hamster);
Mystromys (mole mouse); *Lophiomys* (maned rat);
Lemmus (lemming); *Microtus* (vole); *Clethrionomys*
(=*Evotomys*) (bank vole); *Arvicola* (water vole);
Ondatra (muskrat); *Rattus* (=*Epimys*) (rat);
Mastomys (multimammate rat, coucha rat);
Apodemus (wood mouse); *Mus* (house mouse);
Gerbillus (gerbil); *Meriones* (jird); *Spalax* (mole
rat); *Glis* (=*Myoxus*), *Muscardinus* (dormice);
Zapus (jumping mouse); *Dipus* (jerboa); *Pedetes*
(jumping hare)

Sub-order Hʏsᴛʀɪᴄᴏᴍᴏʀᴘʜᴀ

Cavia (guinea pig); *Hydrochoerus* (capybara);
Chinchilla (chinchilla); *Myocastor* (coypu); *Hystrix*
(porcupine)

Order **CETACEA**

Sub-order Oᴅᴏɴᴛᴏᴄᴇᴛɪ

Mesoplodon (beaked whale); *Physeter* (sperm
whale); *Delphinus* (dolphin); *Tursiops* (=*Tursio*)
(bottle-nosed dolphin); *Orcinus* (killer whale);
Phocaena (porpoise)

Sub-order Mʏsᴛɪᴄᴇᴛɪ

Rhachianectes (grey whale); *Balaenoptera* (ror-
qual); *Sibbaldus* (blue whale)

Order **CARNIVORA**

Sub-order Fɪssɪᴘᴇᴅᴀ

Canis (wolf, dog, jackal); *Vulpes* (fox); *Ursus*
(bear); *Thalarctos* (polar bear); *Procyon* (raccoon);
Potos (kinkajou); *Ailurus* (panda); *Ailuropoda*
(giant panda); *Mustela* (=*Putorius*) (ferret, weasel,
mink, ermine, polecat, stoat); *Martes* (marten,
sable); *Meles* (badger); *Taxidea* (American badger);
Spilogale (spotted skunk); *Lutra* (otter); *Herpestes*
(mongoose); *Hyaena* (striped hyaena); *Viverra*
(civet); *Felis* (cat); *Felis* (=*Puma*) (mountain lion,
cougar); *Panthera* (=*Leo*) (lion); *Panthera*
(=*Tigris*) (tiger); *Panthera* (=*Jaguarius*) (jaguar);
Panthera (panther, leopard); *Acinonyx* (cheetah)

Order **PINNIPEDIA**
>   *Otaria* (sea lion); *Zalophus* (Californian sea lion); *Odobenus* (walrus); *Phoca* (seal); *Halichoerus* (grey seal, Atlantic seal); *Mirounga* (elephant seal)

Order **TUBULIDENTATA**
>   *Orycteropus* (aardvark)

Order **PROBOSCIDEA**
>   *Loxodonta* (African elephant); *Elephas* (Asiatic elephant)

Order **HYRACOIDEA**
>   *Dendrohyrax* (tree hyrax); *Procavia* (coney)

Order **SIRENIA**
>   *Dugong* (dugong); *Trichechus* (manatee)

Order **PERISSODACTYLA**
>   Sub-order HIPPOMORPHA
>   *Equus* (horse, donkey, zebra)
>   Sub-order CERATOMORPHA
>   *Tapirus* (tapir); *Rhinoceros, Diceros, Ceratotherium* (rhinoceroses)

Order **ARTIODACTYLA**
>   Sub-order SUIFORMES
>   *Sus* (pig); *Tayassu* (peccary); *Phacochoerus* (wart hog); *Hippopotamus* (hippopotamus)
>   Sub-order TYLOPODA
>   *Lama* (= *Auchenia*) (llama, alpaca, vicuna, guanaco); *Camelus* (camel, dromedary)
>   Sub-order RUMINANTIA
>   *Tragulus* (chevrotain); *Moschus* (musk deer); *Dama* (fallow deer); *Cervus* (red deer, wapiti, American 'elk'); *Alces* (European elk, moose); *Rangifer* (reindeer, caribou); *Okapia* (okapi); *Giraffa* (giraffe); *Taurotragus* (eland); *Bubalus* (buffalo); *Bos* (cattle); *Bison* (bison, American 'buffalo'); *Hippotragus* (roan antelope); *Antilope* (Indian antelope); *Gazella* (gazelle); *Rupicapra* (chamois); *Ovibos* (musk ox); *Capra* (goat); *Ovis* (sheep)

APPENDIX I. FURTHER READING

THE classifications in Chapter III are based on the references given below, except in two cases, the Parazoa (by Burton) and the Platyhelminthes (by Baer and Dawes). The references, which also contain detailed information about the systematics of the various groups, were compiled in consultation with the specialists mentioned in Appendix II. They differed in their approach, which explains why the list is, in some respects, heterogeneous. Another, but unimportant, cause of heterogeneity is the method of referring to articles in general text-books such as Grassé's *Traité de Zoologie*. In the first two volumes (actually fascicules) of this work, there are articles on the Protozoa by nine authors. These are referred to as Grassé (1952, 1953), and the same policy has been adopted in analogous cases. When one or only a few authors were concerned with a group, as in the case of the Onychophora, the reference is given as Cuénot (1949a) and not Grassé (1949).

Further references will be found in the books and papers listed below. The Zoological Record and Smart & Taylor (1953) are additional and invaluable sources of information.

PROTOZOA
    General   Grassé (1952, 1953); Kudo (1954); Smart & Taylor (1953, pp. 4–16)
    Ciliata   Corliss (1956, 1957, 1959)
MESOZOA   Hyman (1940); Stunkard (1954)
PARAZOA   Hyman (1940, 1959); Jewell (1959)
CNIDARIA
    General   Hyman (1940, 1959); Moore (1956)
    Hydrozoa   Fraser (1937, 1944); Russell (1953); Totton (1954)
    Scyphozoa   Mayer (1910)
    Anthozoa   Carlgren (1949); Stephenson (1928, 1935); Vaughan & Wells (1943)
CTENOPHORA   Hyman (1940, 1959); Mayer (1912)
PLATYHELMINTHES
    General   Baer (1951); Hyman (1951a, 1959)
    Turbellaria   Ferguson (1954); Luther (1955)
    Cestoda   Wardle & McLeod (1952); Yamaguti (1960)
    Trematoda   Dawes (1946); Sproston (1946); Yamaguti (1958)
NEMERTINA   Coe (1943); Hyman (1951a)
ASCHELMINTHES
    Rotifera   Edmondson (1959); Harring (1913); Hudson & Gosse (1886); Hyman (1951b, 1959); Voigt (1957)
    Gastrotricha   Brunson (1950, 1959); Hyman (1951b, 1959)
    Echinoderida   Hyman (1951b, 1959); Lang (1949); Zelinka (1928)
    Priapulida   Cuénot (1922a); Dawydoff (1959c); Hyman (1951b, 1959)
    Nematomorpha   Chitwood (1959); Hyman (1951b, 1959)
    Nematoda   Chitwood & Allen (1959); Chitwood & Chitwood (1950); Goffart (1951); Goodey (1951); Thorne (1949)
ACANTHOCEPHALA Hyman (1951b, 1959)
ENTOPROCTA   Brien (1959); Hyman (1951b, 1959)
POLYZOA   Bassler (1953); Brien (1960); Hyman (1959); Rogick (1959)
PHORONIDA   Dawydoff & Grassé (1959); Forneris (1957); Hyman (1959)
BRACHIOPODA   de Beauchamp (1960a); Hyman (1959); Muir-Wood (1955); Roger (1952); Williams (1956)
MOLLUSCA
    General   Grassé (1960); Morton (1958); Thiele (1931, 1935)
    Polyplacophora   Fischer-Piette & Franc (1960b); Hoffmann (1929–1930); Tryon & Pilsbry (1892–1893)

Aplacophora   Fischer-Piette & Franc (1960*a*); Hoffmann (1929)

Monoplacophora   Lemche & Wingstrand (1960)

Gastropoda   Hoffmann (1932–1940); Lemche (1948); Tesch (1946–1949)

Bivalvia   Franc (1960)

Cephalopoda   Adam (1952); Chun (1908, 1910); Robson (1929–1932); Sasaki (1929)

SIPUNCULOIDEA   Hyman (1959); Tetry (1959)

ECHIUROIDEA   Cuénot (1922*b*); Dawydoff (1959*b*)

ANNELIDA

General   Grassé (1959)

Polychaeta   Dawydoff (1959*a*); Fauvel (1923, 1927, 1959)

Myzostomaria   Prenant (1959); von Stummer-Traunfels (1926)

Oligochaeta   Avel (1959); Cernosvitov & Evans (1947); Dawydoff (1959*a*); Goodnight (1959); Stephenson (1930)

Hirudinea   Dawydoff (1959*a*); Harant & Grassé (1959); Harding (1910); Harding & Moore (1927); Mann & Watson (1954); Moore (1959)

Archiannelida   de Beauchamp (1959)

ARTHROPODA

Onychophora   Bouvier (1905); Cuénot (1949*a*)

Pauropoda   Attems (1926*b*); Verhoeff (1934)

Diplopoda   Attems (1926*c*, 1937–1940)

Chilopoda   Attems (1926*d*–1930)

Symphyla   Attems (1926*a*); Edwards (1959); Verhoeff (1933)

Insecta   Imms (1957); Smart & Taylor (1953, pp. 42–73)

Crustacea

General   Calman (1909); Kükenthal & Krumbach (1927)

Cephalocarida   Sanders (1957)

Copepoda   Wilson (1932)

Mystacocarida   Delamare Deboutteville (1953)

Cirripedia   Krüger (1940)

Malacostraca   Bronn's (1940–1959)

Merostomata   Fage (1949*a*)

Arachnida   Baker & Wharton (1952); Grassé (1949); Hughes (1959); Kaston & Kaston (1953); Locket & Millidge (1951, 1953); Nuttall *et al.* (1908–1926); Petrunkevitch (1928, 1949); Vachon (1952)

Pycnogonida   Fage (1949*b*); Hedgpeth (1947); Helfer & Schlottke (1935)

Pentastomida   Cuénot (1949*c*); Heymons (1935)

Tardigrada   Cuénot (1949*b*); Marcus (1936, 1959)

CHAETOGNATHA   de Beauchamp (1960*b*); Fraser (1957); Hyman (1959)

POGONOPHORA   Hartman (1954); Hyman (1959); Ivanov (1960)

ECHINODERMATA

General   Cuénot (1948); Hyman (1955)

Echinoidea   Durham & Melville (1957); Mortensen (1928–1951)

CHORDATA

Hemichordata   Burdon-Jones (1956); Dawydoff (1948); Hyman (1959)

Urochordata   Berrill (1950); Harant (1948)

Cephalochordata   Drach (1948); Franz (1922)

Vertebrata

Marsipobranchii   Berg (1947); Fontaine (1958); Regan (1936)

Selachii   Arambourg & Bertin (1958*a*); Berg (1947); Regan (1929*b*, 1936)

Bradyodonti   Arambourg & Bertin (1958*b*); Berg (1947)

Pisces	Berg (1947); Grassé (1958); Regan (1929*a*, 1936)
Amphibia	
General	Boulenger (1882); Noble (1931)
Salientia	Griffiths (1959)
Gymnophiona	Nieden (1913)
Reptilia	
General	Bellairs (1957); Schmidt & Inger (1957)
Rhynchocephalia	von Wettstein (1931–1937)
Testudines	Carr (1952); Loveridge & Williams (1957); Pope (1935)
Crocodylia	Mertens & Wermuth (1955)
Squamata	Bellairs & Underwood (1951); Bogert & del Campo (1956); Boulenger (1920–1921); McDowell & Bogert (1954)
Aves	Mayr & Amadon (1951); Peters (1931–1951); Stresemann (1959); Wetmore (1951)
Mammalia	Grassé (1955); Simpson (1945)

APPENDIX II. ACKNOWLEDGMENTS

I AM most grateful to those scientists, mentioned below, who have been good enough to help me. R. B. Freeman gave invaluable help with Chapter III, as did Dr. J. Smart with the Insecta. In addition, I am indebted to George Rylands for advice about Chapter I and to Mrs. J. N. Thomson, who typed this book with exemplary patience and efficiency. I wish also to thank the Agricultural Research Council for support.

Ch. I	Prof. C. F. A. Pantin, F.R.S.; Dr. K. A. Joysey.
Ch. III	
PROTOZOA	Dr. C. A. Hoare, F.R.S.
PARAZOA	Dr. Maurice Burton, D.Sc.
CNIDARIA	Dr. W. J. Rees, D.Sc.; Dr. F. S. Russell, F.R.S.; Prof. T. A. Stephenson, F.R.S.
CTENOPHORA	Dr. W. J. Rees, D.Sc.; Dr. F. S. Russell, F.R.S.
PLATYHELMINTHES	Prof. J. G. Baer; Dr. B. Dawes; Mr. S. Prudhoe; Dr. F. G. Rees.
NEMERTINA	Prof. C. F. A. Pantin, F.R.S.; Mr. S. Prudhoe.
ASCHELMINTHES	
Rotifera	Miss A. Edwards; Mr. A. L. Galliford.
Gastrotricha	Mr. S. Prudhoe.
Echinoderida	Mr. S. Prudhoe.
Priapulida	Mr. S. Prudhoe; Dr. A. C. Stephen.
Nematoda	Prof. B. G. Peters; Mr. S. Prudhoe.
Nematomorpha	Mr. S. Prudhoe.
ACANTHOCEPHALA	Mr. S. Prudhoe.
ENTOPROCTA	Dr. A. B. Hastings.
POLYZOA	Dr. A. B. Hastings.
BRACHIOPODA	Dr. G. Owen, D.Sc.; Dr. H. M. Muir-Wood, D.Sc.
MOLLUSCA	Prof. A. Graham, D.Sc.; Dr. D. Parry; Dr. W. J. Rees, D.Sc.; Prof. C. M. Yonge, F.R.S.
SIPUNCULOIDEA	Dr. A. C. Stephen; Dr. D. P. Wilson, D.Sc.
ECHIUROIDEA	Dr. A. C. Stephen; Dr. D. P. Wilson, D.Sc.
ANNELIDA	Dr. R. Phillips Dales; Miss A. Edwards; Dr. K. H. Mann; Dr. B. I. Roots; Mr. N. Tebble; Dr. D. P. Wilson, D.Sc.
ARTHROPODA	
Onychophora	Dr. G. O. Evans; Dr. S. M. Manton, F.R.S.
Pauropoda	Mr. J. G. Blower; Dr. G. O. Evans.
Diplopoda	Mr. J. G. Blower; Dr. G. O. Evans.
Chilopoda	Mr. J. G. Blower; Dr. G. O. Evans; Dr. S. M. Manton, F.R.S.
Symphyla	Mr. J. G. Blower; Dr. G. O. Evans.
Insecta	Dr. W. E. China, C.B.E., Sc.D., and the staff of the Entomology Department, the British Museum (Natural History); Dr. H. E. Hinton; Prof. O. W. Richards, F.R.S.; the Hon. Miriam Rothschild; Dr. G. Salt, F.R.S.; Dr. J. Smart, D.Sc.
Crustacea	Dr. I. Gordon, D.Sc.; Dr. J. Green; Dr. J. P. Harding.
Merostomata	Dr. G. O. Evans.
Arachnida	Dr. J. L. Cloudsley-Thompson; Dr. G. O. Evans.
Pycnogonida	Dr. G. O. Evans.
Pentastomida	Dr. J. L. Cloudsley-Thompson; Dr. G. O. Evans.
Tardigrada	Dr. J. L. Cloudsley-Thompson; Dr. G. O. Evans.
CHAETOGNATHA	Dr. F. S. Russell, F.R.S.

ECHINODERMATA	Miss A. M. Clark; Prof. J. E. Smith, F.R.S.; Dr. H. G. Vevers, M.B.E.
CHORDATA	
Hemichordata	Dr. C. Burdon-Jones.
Urochordata	Prof. J. Berrill, F.R.S.; Dr. R. H. Millar.
Cephalochordata	Dr. J. E. Webb, D.Sc.
Vertebrata	
Marsipobranchii	Mr. N. B. Marshall; Dr. E. Trewavas, D.Sc.
Selachii	Mr. N. B. Marshall; Dr. E. Trewavas, D.Sc.
Bradyodonti	Mr. N. B. Marshall; Dr. E. Trewavas, D.Sc.
Pisces	Mr. N. B. Marshall; Dr. E. Trewavas, D.Sc.
Amphibia	Miss A. G. C. Grandison.
Reptilia	Mr. J. C. Battersby, B.E.M.
Aves	Dr. T. Clay, D.Sc.; Dr. W. H. Thorpe, F.R.S.
Mammalia	Dr. P. Crowcroft; Dr. W. C. Osman Hill, M.D., F.R.S.E.; Mr. G. B. Stratton, M.B.E., A.L.S.

APPENDIX III. REFERENCES

ADAM, W. (1952) Céphalopodes. *Expédition Océanographique Belge dans les Eaux Côtières Africaines de l'Atlantique Sud (1948–1949)*, **3**, Fasc. 3.

ARAMBOURG, C. & BERTIN, L. (1958a) *Traité de Zoologie*,[1] **13**, Fasc. 3, 2016–2056.

—— —— (1958b) *Traité de Zoologie*, **13**, Fasc. 3, 2057–2067.

ATTEMS, C.

—— (1926a) *Handb. Zool., Berl.*, **4**, 1, 11–19.

—— (1926b) *Handb. Zool., Berl.*, **4**, 1, 20–28.

—— (1926c) *Handb. Zool., Berl.*, **4**, 1, 29–238.

—— (1926d) *Handb. Zool., Berl.*, **4**, 1, 239–402.

—— (1929) *Das Tierreich*,[2] Lief. 52.

—— (1930) *Das Tierreich*, Lief. 54.

—— (1937–1940) *Das Tierreich*, Liefn. 68, 69 & 70.

AVEL, M. (1959) *Traité de Zoologie*, **5**, Fasc. 1, 224–470.

BAER, J. G. (1951) *Ecology of Animal Parasites*. University of Illinois Press, Urbana.

BAKER, E. W. & WHARTON, G. W. (1952) *An Introduction to Acarology*. Macmillan, New York.

BASSLER, R. S. (1953) *Treatise on Invertebrate Paleontology*,[3] Part G, *Bryozoa*.

DE BEAUCHAMP, P. (1959) *Traité de Zoologie*, **5**, Fasc. 1, 197–223.

—— (1960a) *Traité de Zoologie*, **5**, Fasc. 2, 1380–1430.

—— (1960b) *Traité de Zoologie*, **5**, Fasc. 2, 1500–1520.

BELLAIRS, A. d'A. (1957) *Reptiles*. Hutchinson, London.

BELLAIRS, A. d'A. & UNDERWOOD, G. (1951) The Origin of Snakes. *Biol. Rev.*, **26**, 193–237.

BERG, L. S. (1947) *Classification of Fishes, both Recent and Fossil*. J. W. Edwards, Ann Arbor, Michigan.

BERRILL, N. J. (1950) *The Tunicata*. London, printed for the Ray Society.

BOGERT, C. M. & CAMPO, R. M. DEL (1956) The Gila-monster and its Allies. The Relationships, Habits and Behaviour of the Lizards of the Family Helodermatidae. *Bull. Amer. Mus. nat. Hist.*, **109**, 1–238.

BOULENGER, G. A. (1882) *Catalogue of the Batrachia Gradientia S. Caudata and Batrachia Apoda in the Collection of the British Museum*, 2nd edition. London, printed for the Trustees of the British Museum.

—— (1920–1921) *Monograph of the Lacertidae*, Vols. I & II. London, printed for the Trustees of the British Museum.

BOUVIER, E. (1905) Monographie des Onychophores. *Ann. Sci. nat., Zool.*, (9), **2**.

BRIEN, P. (1959) *Traité de Zoologie*, **5**, Fasc. 1, 927–1007.

—— (1960) *Traité de Zoologie*, **5**, Fasc. 2, 1053–1335.

BRONN's *Klassen* (1940–1959) **5**, Abt. 1, B. 4–7.

BRUNSON, R. B. (1950) An Introduction to the Taxonomy of the Gastrotricha with a Study of Eighteen Species from Michigan. *Trans. Amer. micr. Soc.*, **69**, 325–352.

—— (1959) *Fresh-water Biology*,[4] 406–419.

BURDON-JONES, C. (1956) *Handb. Zool., Berl.*, **3** (2, Supp.) 57–78.

CALMAN, W. T. (1909) *A Treatise on Zoology* (ed. Sir Ray Lankester), Part 7, *Crustacea*. Adam & Charles Black, London.

CARLGREN, O. (1949) A Survey of the Ptychodactiaria, Corallimorpharia and Actiniaria. *K. svenska VetenskAkad. Handl.* (4), **1**, 1.

CARR, A. (1952) *Handbook of Turtles. The Turtles of the United States, Canada and Baja California*. Comstock Publishing Associates, New York.

CERNOSVITOV, L. & EVANS, A. C. (1947) Lumbricidae (Annelida). The Linnaean Society of London, Synopses of the British Fauna, No. 6.

---

[1] i.e. Grassé, P.-P. *Traité de Zoologie*. Masson, Paris.
[2] i.e. *Das Tierreich*. Walter de Gruyter, Berlin & Leipzig.
[3] i.e. Moore, R. C. *Treatise on Invertebrate Paleontology*. Geological Society of America & University of Kansas Press.
[4] i.e. Edmondson, W. T. *Fresh-water Biology*. (Ward & Whipple). John Wiley, New York.

CHITWOOD, B. G. (1959) *Fresh-water Biology*, 402–405.

CHITWOOD, B. G. & ALLEN, M. W. (1959) *Fresh-water Biology*, 368–401.

CHITWOOD, B. G. & CHITWOOD, M. B. (1950) *An Introduction to Nematology*. Monumental Printing Company.

CHUN, C. (1908) Über Cephalopoden der Deutschen Tiefsee-Expedition. *Zool. Anz.*, **33**, 86–89.

—— (1910) Die Cephalopoden. I. Oegopsida. *Wiss. Ergebn. 'Valdivia'*, **18**, 1–402.

COE, W. R. (1943) Biology of the Nemerteans of the Atlantic Coast of North America. *Trans. Conn. Acad. Arts Sci.*, **35**, 129–328.

CORLISS, J. O. (1956) On the Evolution & Systematics of Ciliated Protozoa. *Systematic Zoology*, **5**, 68–91, 121–140.

—— (1957) Nomenclatural History of the Higher Taxa in the Sub phylum Ciliophora. *Arch. Protistenk.*, **102**, 113–146.

—— (1959) An Illustrated Key to the Higher Groups of the Ciliated Protozoa with Definition of Terms. *J. Protozoology*, **6**, 265–284.

CUÉNOT, L. (1922a) *Faune de France*,[1] **4**, 25.

—— (1922b) *Faune de France*, **4**, 18–24.

—— (1948) *Traité de Zoologie*, **11**, 3–363.

—— (1949a) *Traité de Zoologie*, **6**, 3–37.

—— (1949b) *Traité de Zoologie*, **6**, 39–59.

—— (1949c) *Traité de Zoologie*, **6**, 61–75.

DAWES, B. (1946) *The Trematoda*. Cambridge University Press.

DAWYDOFF, C. (1948) *Traité de Zoologie*, **11**, 367–499.

—— (1959a) *Traité de Zoologie*, **5**, Fasc. 1, 594–686.

—— (1959b) *Traité de Zoologie*, **5**, Fasc. 1, 855–907.

—— (1959c) *Traité de Zoologie*, **5**, Fasc. 1, 908–926.

DAWYDOFF, C. & GRASSÉ, P.-P. (1959) *Traité de Zoologie*, **5**, Fasc. 1, 1008–1053.

DELAMARE DEBOUTTEVILLE, CL. (1953) Recherches sur l'écologie et la répartition du Mystacocaride *Derocheilocaris remanei* Delamare et Chappuis, en Mediterranée. *Vie et Milieu*, **4**, 321–380.

DRACH, P. (1948) *Traité de Zoologie*, **11**, 931–1037.

DURHAM, J. W. & MELVILLE, R. V. (1957) A Classification of Echinoids. *J. Paleont.*, **31**, 242–272.

EDMONDSON, W. T. (1959) *Fresh-water Biology*, 420–494.

EDWARDS, C. A. (1959) A Revision of the British Symphyla. *Proc. zool. Soc. Lond.*, **132**, 403–439.

FAGE, L. (1949a) *Traité de Zoologie*, **6**, 219–262.

—— (1949b) *Traité de Zoologie*, **6**, 906–941.

FAUVEL, P. (1923) *Faune de France*, **5**.

—— (1927) *Faune de France*, **16**.

—— (1959) *Traité de Zoologie*, **5**, Fasc. 1, 13–196.

FERGUSON, F. F. (1954) Monograph of the Macrostomine worms [sic] of Turbellaria. *Trans. Amer. micr. Soc.*, **73**, 137–164.

FISCHER-PIETTE, E. & FRANC, A. (1960a) *Traité de Zoologie*, **5**, Fasc. 2, 1655–1700.

—— (1960b) *Traité de Zoologie*, **5**, Fasc. 2, 1701–1785.

FISHER, W. K. (1950) The Sipunculid Genus *Phascolosoma*. *Ann. Mag. nat. Hist.* (12), **3**, 547–552.

FONTAINE, M. (1958) *Traité de Zoologie*, **13**, Fasc. 1, 13–172.

FORNERIS, L. (1957) Phoronidea. *Fiches d'identification du zooplancton*, Sheet 69. Conseil international pour l'exploration de la mer.

FRANC, A. (1960) *Traité de Zoologie*, **5**, Fasc. 2, 1845–2133.

FRANZ, V. (1922) Kurzer Bericht über systematische Acranierstudien. *Zool. Anz.*, **54**, 241–249.

[1] i.e. *Faune de France*. Paul Lechevalier, Paris.

FRASER, C. McL. (1937) *Hydroids of the Pacific Coast of Canada and the United States.* University of Toronto Press.

—— (1944) *Hydroids of the Atlantic Coast of North America.* University of Toronto Press.

FRASER, J. H. (1957) Chaetognatha. *Fiches d'identification du zooplancton*, Sheet 1 (1st revision). Conseil international pour l'exploration de la mer.

GOFFART, H. (1951) *Nematoden der Kulturpflanzen Europas.* Paul Parey, Berlin.

GOODEY, T. (1951) *Soil and Freshwater Nematodes.* Methuen, London.

GOODNIGHT, C. J. (1959) *Fresh-water Biology*, 522–537.

GRASSÉ, P.-P. (1949) *Traité de Zoologie*, **6**, 263–892.

—— (1952, 1953) *Traité de Zoologie*, **1**, Fascs. 1–2.

—— (1955) *Traité de Zoologie*, **17**, Fascs. 1–2.

—— (1958) *Traité de Zoologie*, **13**, Fascs. 1–3.

—— (1959) *Traité de Zoologie*, **5**, Fasc. 1, 1–686.

—— (1960) *Traité de Zoologie*, **5**, Fasc. 2, 1623–2164.

GRIFFITHS, I. (1959) The Phylogeny of *Sminthillus limbatus* and the Status of the Brachycephalidae (Amphibia Salientia). *Proc. zool. Soc. Lond.*, **132**, 457–487.

GURNEY, R. (1933) *British Fresh-water Copepoda*, Vol. 3. London, printed for the Ray Society.

HARANT, H. (1948) *Traité de Zoologie*, **11**, 895–919.

HARANT, H. & GRASSÉ, P.-P. (1959) *Traité de Zoologie*, **5**, Fasc. 1, 471–593.

HARDING, W. A. (1910) A Revision of the British Leeches. *Parasitology*, **3**, 130–201.

HARDING, W. A. & MOORE, J. P. (1927) *The Fauna of British India. Hirudinea.* Taylor & Francis, London.

HARRING, H. K. (1913) Synopsis of the Rotatoria. *Bull. U.S. nat. Mus.*, **81**.

HARTMAN, O. (1954) Pogonophora Johansson, 1938. *Systematic Zoology*, **3**, 183–185.

HEDGPETH, J. W. (1947) On the Evolutionary Significance of the Pycnogonida. *Smithson. misc. Coll.*, **106**, 18.

HELFER, H. & SCHLOTTKE, E. (1935) *Bronn's Klassen*, **5**, Abt. 4, B.2, 1–314.

HEYMONS, R. (1935) *Bronn's Klassen*, **5**, Abt. 4, B.1.

HOFFMANN, H. (1929) *Bronn's Klassen*, **3**, Abt. 1, 1–134.

—— (1929–1930) *Bronn's Klassen*, **3**, Abt. 1, 135–382.

—— (1932–1940) *Bronn's Klassen*, **3**, Abt. 2, B.3.

HUDSON, C. T. & GOSSE, P. H. (1886) *The Rotifera.* Longmans, Green, London.

HUGHES, T. E. (1959) *Mites, or the Acari.* University of London, The Athlone Press.

HYMAN, L. H. (1940) *The Invertebrates.*[1] Vol. I. *Protozoa through Ctenophora.*

—— (1951a) *The Invertebrates.* Vol. II. *Platyhelminthes and Rhynchocoela.*

—— (1951b) *The Invertebrates.* Vol. III. *Acanthocephala, Aschelminthes and Entoprocta.*

—— (1955) *The Invertebrates.* Vol. IV. *Echinodermata.*

—— (1959) *The Invertebrates.* Vol. V. *Smaller Coelomate Groups.*

IMMS, A. D. (1957) *A General Textbook of Entomology.* Methuen, London.

IVANOV, A. V. (1960) *Traité de Zoologie*, **5**, Fasc. 2, 1521–1622.

JEWELL, M. (1959) *Fresh-water Biology*, 298–312.

JOHNSON, S. (1755) *A Dictionary of the English Language.* W. Strahan, London.

KASTON, B. J. & KASTON, E. (1953) *How to know the Spiders.* W. C. Brown, Dubuque, Iowa.

KRÜGER, P. (1940) *Bronn's Klassen*, **5**, Abt. 1, B.3, 1–560.

KUDO, R. R. (1954) *Protozoology.* C. C. Thomas, U.S.A.

KÜKENTHAL, W. & KRUMBACH, T. (1927) *Handb. Zool., Berl.*, **3**, 1, 277–1158.

LANG, K. (1949) Echinoderida. *Further zool. Res. Swed. Antarct. Exp.*, **4**, Part 2.

LEMCHE, H. (1948) Northern and Arctic Tectibranch Gastropods. I. The Larval Shells. II. A Revision of the Cephalaspid Species. *K. danske vidensk. Selsk., biol.*, **5**, 3.

LEMCHE, H. & WINGSTRAND, K. G. (1960) *Traité de Zoologie*, **5**, Fasc. 2, 1787–1821.

LOCKET, G. H. & MILLIDGE, A. F. (1951, 1953) *British Spiders.* London, printed for the Ray Society.

---

[1] i.e. Hyman, L. H. *The Invertebrates*. McGraw-Hill, New York.

LOVERIDGE, A. & WILLIAMS, E. E. (1957) Revision of the African Tortoises and Turtles of the Sub order Cryptodira. *Bull. Mus. comp. Zool. Harv.*, **115**, 163–557.

LUTHER, A. (1955) Die Dalyelliiden (Turbellaria Neorhabdocoela). Eine Monographie. *Acta zool. fenn.*, **87**.

MANN, K. H. & WATSON, E. V. (1954) A Key to the British Freshwater Leeches. *Freshwater Biological Association Scientific Publication* No. 14.

MARCUS, E. (1936) *Das Tierreich*. Lief. 66.

—— (1959) *Fresh-water Biology*, 508–521.

MAYER, A. G. (1910) Medusae of the World. The Scyphomedusae. *Publ. Carneg. Instn.*, No. 109, **3**, 499–735.

—— (1912) Ctenophores of the Atlantic Coast of North America. *Publ. Carneg. Instn.*, No. 162.

MAYR, E. & AMADON, D. (1951) A Classification of Recent Birds. *Amer. Mus. Novit.*, No. 1496.

MAYR, E., LINSLEY, E. G. & USINGER, R. L. (1953) *Methods and Principles of Systematic Zoology*. McGraw-Hill, New York.

MCDOWELL, S. B. & BOGERT, C. M. (1954) The Systematic Position of *Lanthanotus* and the Affinities of the Anguinomorphan Lizards. *Bull. Amer. Mus. nat. Hist.*, **105**, 1, 1–142.

MERTENS, R. & WERMUTH, H. (1955) Die rezenten Schildkröten, Krokodile und Brückenechsen, eine kritische Liste der heute lebenden Arten und Rassen. *Zool. Jb.*, **83**, 323–440.

MOORE, J. P. (1959) *Fresh-water Biology*, 542–557.

MOORE, R. C. (1956) *Treatise on Invertebrate Paleontology*, Part F, *Coelenterata*.

MORTENSEN, TH. (1928–1951) *A Monograph of the Echinoidea*. C. A. Reitzel, Copenhagen.

MORTON, J. E. (1958) *Molluscs*. Hutchinson, London.

MUIR-WOOD, H. M. (1955) *A History of the Classification of the Phylum Brachiopoda*. London, printed for the Trustees of the British Museum.

NEAVE, S. A. (1939–1950) *Nomenclator Zoologicus*. The Zoological Society of London.

NIEDEN, FR. (1913) *Das Tierreich*, Lief. 37.

NOBLE, G. K. (1931) *The Biology of the Amphibia*. McGraw-Hill, New York.

NUTTALL, G. H. F., WARBURTON, C., COOPER, W. F. & ROBINSON, L. E. (1908–1926) *Ticks. A Monograph of the Ixodoidea*. Cambridge University Press.

PETERS, J. L. (1931–1951) *Check-list of Birds of the World*. Harvard University Printing Office, Cambridge, U.S.A.

PETRUNKEVITCH, A. (1928) Systema Aranearum. *Trans. Conn. Acad. Arts Sci.*, **29**, 1–270.

—— (1949) A Study of Palaeozoic Arachnida. *Trans. Conn. Acad. Arts Sci.*, **37**, 69–315.

POPE, C. H. (1935) The Reptiles of China, Turtles, Crocodilians, Snakes, Lizards. *Nat. Hist. Centr. Asia*, **10**.

PRENANT, M. (1959) *Traité de Zoologie*, **5**, Fasc. 1, 714–784.

REGAN, C. T. (1929*a*) *Encyclopaedia Britannica*, 14th edition (actual), London, **9**, 305–328.

—— (1929*b*) *Encyclopaedia Britannica*, 14th edition, London, **20**, 292–295.

—— (1936) *Natural History*. Ward, Lock, London.

REID, D. M. (1925) *Animal Classification and Distribution*. Charles Griffin, London.

ROBSON, G. C. (1929–1932) *A Monograph of the Recent Cephalopoda*, Parts I & II. London, printed for the Trustees of the British Museum.

ROGER, J. (1952) *Traité de Paléontologie* (ed. J. Piveteau), **2**, 3–160. Masson, Paris.

ROGICK, M. D. (1959) *Fresh-water Biology*, 495–507.

RUSSELL, F. S. (1953) *The Medusae of the British Isles*. Cambridge University Press.

SANDERS, H. L. (1957) The Cephalocarida and Crustacean Phylogeny. *Systematic Zoology*, **6**, 112–128.

SASAKI, M. (1929) A Monograph of the Dibranchiate Cephalopods of the Japanese and Adjacent Waters. *J. Fac. Agric. Hokkaido Univ.*, Suppl. to Vol. 20, 1928.

SCHMIDT, K. P. & INGER, R. F. (1957) *Living Reptiles of the World*. Hamish Hamilton, London.

SIMPSON, G. G. (1945) The Principles of Classification and a Classification of Mammals. *Bull. Amer. Mus. nat. Hist.*, **85**.

SMART, J. & TAYLOR, G. (1953) *Bibliography of Key Works for the Identification of British Fauna and Flora*. The Systematics Association, London.

SPECTOR, W. S. (1956) *Handbook of Biological Data*. W. B. Saunders, Philadelphia & London.,

SPROSTON, N. G. (1946) A Synopsis of the Monogenetic Trematodes. *Trans. zool. Soc. Lond.*, **25**, 185–600.

STEPHENSON, J. (1930) *The Oligochaeta*. Oxford, at the Clarendon Press.

STEPHENSON, T. A. (1928, 1935) *The British Sea Anemones*. London, printed for the Ray Society.

STRESEMANN, E. (1959) The Status of Avian Systematics and its Unsolved Problems. *Auk*, **76**, 269–280.

STUMMER-TRAUNFELS, R. VON (1926) *Handb. Zool.*, *Berl.*, **3**, 1 (2), 132–210.

STUNKARD, H. W. (1954) Life-history and Systematic Relations of the Mesozoa. *Quart. Rev. Biol.*, **29**, 230–244.

TESCH, J. J. (1946) The Thecosomatous Pteropods. I. The Atlantic. *Dana Rep.*, **28**.

—— (1948) The Thecosomatous Pteropods. II. The Indo-Pacific. *Dana Rep.*, **30**.

—— (1949) Heteropoda. *Dana Rep.*, **34**.

TETRY, A. (1959) *Traité de Zoologie*, **5**, Fasc. 1, 785–854; mlxviii–mlxxxi.

THIELE, J. (1931, 1935) *Handbuch der Systematischen Weichtierkunde*. Gustav Fischer, Jena.

THORNE, G. (1949) On the Classification of the Tylenchida, new order (Nematoda, Phasmidia). *Proc. helm. Soc. Wash.*, **16**, 37–73.

TOTTON, A. K. (1954) Siphonophora of the Indian Ocean, together with Systematic and Biological Notes on Related Specimens from other Oceans. *'Discovery' Rep.*, **27**, 7–162.

TRYON, G. W. & PILSBRY, H. A. (1892–1893) Monograph of the Polyplacophora. *Manual Conch.*, **14**, **15**.

VACHON, M. (1952) *Études sur les Scorpions*. Institut Pasteur d'Algérie, Alger.

VAUGHAN, T. W. & WELLS, J. W. (1943) Revision of the Sub orders, Families, and Genera of the Scleractinia. *Geological Society of America Special Paper* No. 44.

VERHOEFF, K. W. (1933) *Bronn's Klassen*, **5**, Abt. 2, B.3 (1).

VOIGT, M. (1957) *Rotatoria*. Gebrüder Borntraeger, Berlin-Nikolassee.

WARDLE, R. A. & MCLEOD, J. A. (1952) *The Zoology of Tapeworms*. University of Minnesota Press, Minneapolis.

WETMORE, A. (1951) A Revised Classification for the Birds of the World. *Smithson. misc. Coll.*, **117**, No. 4.

WETTSTEIN, O. VON (1931–1937) *Handb. Zool.*, *Berl.*, **7**, 1 (2), 1–235.

WILLIAMS, A. (1956) The Calcareous Shell of the Brachiopoda and its Importance to their Classification. *Biol. Rev.*, **31**, 243–287.

WILSON, C. B. (1932) The Copepods of the Woods Hole Region, Massachusetts. *Bull. U.S. nat. Mus.*, No. 158.

YAMAGUTI, S. (1958) *Systema Helminthum*. Vol. I. *The Digenetic Trematodes of Vertebrates*. Interscience Publishers, New York.

—— (1960) *Systema Helminthum*. Vol. II. *The Cestodes of Vertebrates*. Interscience Publishers, New York.

ZELINKA, K. (1928) *Monographie der Echinodera*. Wilhelm Engelmann, Leipzig.

ANIMAL AND GROUP INDEX

ALTHOUGH this Section should be used as an Index, it also provides an abbreviated classification of all genera mentioned. When there are sub-orders in Chapter III, sub-orders and not orders are given after genera in the Index, to help the reader find the genus in which he is interested. Normally, for example in papers, the order and not the sub-order is mentioned when referring to an animal which is not well known.

Starred genera occur in the Index and *not* in Chapter III. When such entries have synonyms worth mentioning, they follow the preferred name, e.g.

Caretta (= *Thallassochelys*), Cryptodira, 41

because there is no other way of finding out that the synonym exists. This does not apply to unstarred entries, as these will also be found in Chapter III, in which some synonyms are mentioned.

aardvark (*Orycteropus*), Tubulidentata, 46
abalone (*Haliotis*), Archaeogastropoda, 21
Acanthamoeba, Amoebina, 7
Acanthephyra, Natantia, 31
Acanthias, see *Squalus*
Acanthis, Passeres, 43
Acanthobdella, Acanthobdellida, 24
Acanthobdellida, 24
Acanthobothrium, Tetraphyllidea, 14
Acanthocephala, 20
Acanthocotyle, Acanthocotyloidea, 13
Acanthocotyloidea, 13
Acanthocystis, Heliozoa, 7
Acanthometra, Radiolaria, 7
Acanthopterygii, 38 (footnote)
Acanthosolenia, Coccolithophorida, 6
Acanthosphaera, Radiolaria, 7
Acanthuroidea, 38
Acanthurus, Acanthuroidea, 38
Acara, see *Aequidens*
Acari, 31
Acarus, Acari, 31
Accipiter, Falconiformes, 42
Accipitres, see Falconiformes
Acerentulus, Protura, 26
Acerina, Percoidea, 38
Achatina, Stylommatophora, 22
Acherontia, Ditrysia, 28
Acheta, Ensifera, 26
Acholoe, Polychaeta, 24
Achroia, Ditrysia, 28
Acidalia, see *Argyreus*
*—, see *Scopula*
Acilius, Adephaga, 28
Acineta, Suctorida, 8
Acineta, see Suctorida
Acinonyx, Fissipeda, 45
Acipenser, Chondrostei, 36

Acipenseriformes, see Chondrostei
Acmaea, Archaeogastropoda, 21
Acoela, 13, 22
acorn worms (Enteropneusta), 34
Acotylea, 13
Acrania, see Cephalochordata
Acricotopus, see *Cricotopus*
Acris, Procoela, 40
Acrocephalus, Passeres, 43
Acrocnida, Ophiurae, 34
Acronicta, Ditrysia, 28
Acropora, Scleractinia, 12
Acrothoracica, 30
Acrotus, Malacichthyes, 39
Actaeon, Pleurocoela, 22
actaeon shell (*Actaeon*), Pleurocoela, 22
Actinia, Actiniaria, 12
Actiniaria, 12
Actinistia, 40
Actinoloba, see *Metridium*
Actinolophus, Heliozoa, 7
Actinomonas, Heliozoa, 7
Actinomyxidia, 8
Actinophrys, Heliozoa, 7
Actinopoda, 7
Actinosphaerium, Heliozoa, 7
Actitis, Charadriiformes, 42
Adamsia, Actiniaria, 12
adder (*Vipera*), Serpentes, 41
Adeleidea, 7
Adelges, Homoptera, 27
Adelina, Adeleidea, 7
Adephaga, 28
Adineta, Bdelloidea, 17
Adocia, Sigmatosclerophora, 10
Aechmophorus, Podicipediformes, 42
Aedes, Nematocera, 28
Aegina, Narcomedusae, 11

Aegypius, Falconiformes, 42
*Aequidens (= *Acara*), Percoidea, 38
Aequorea, Thecata, 11
Aeshna, Anisoptera, 26
African East Coast cattle fever (*Theileria*),
     Haemosporidia, 8
African elephant (*Loxodonta*),
     Proboscidea, 46
African ground squirrel (*Xerus*),
     Sciuromorpha, 45
African tree monkeys (*Cercopithecus*),
     Simiae, 44
Agalma, Siphonophora, 11
Agapornis, Psittaciformes, 43
*Agelaioides, see *Molothrus*
*Agelastica, Polyphaga, 28
Aglantha, Trachymedusae, 11
Agnatha, see Marsipobranchii
*Agriolimax, Stylommatophora, 22
Agrion, Zygoptera, 26
Agriotes, Polyphaga, 28
Ailuropoda, Fissipeda, 45
Ailurus, Fissipeda, 45
Alabes, Alabetoidea, 40
Alabetoidea, 40
Alauda, Passeres, 43
albatross (*Diomedea*),
     Procellariiformes, 42
Alca, Charadriiformes, 42
Alcedo, Coraciiformes, 43
Alces, Ruminantia, 46
Alcippe, Acrothoracica, 30
Alcyonacea, 12
Alcyonella, see *Plumatella*
Alcyonidium, Ctenostomata, 20
Alcyonium, Alcyonacea, 12
alder fly (*Sialis*), Megaloptera, 27
*Alectrion, Stenoglossa, 22
Alepisauroidea, 37
Alepisaurus, Alepisauroidea, 37
Alepocephalus, Clupeoidea, 36
Alligator, Crocodylia, 41
alligator (*Alligator*), Crocodylia, 41
Alloeocoela, 13
Allogromia, Testacea, 7
Allolobophora, Oligochaeta, 24
*Alloteuthis, Decapoda, 23
Allotriognathi, 38
*Alosa, Clupeoidea, 36
alpaca (*Lama*), Tylopoda, 46

Alytes, Opisthocoela, 40
Amaroucium, see *Aplidium*
*Amazilia, Apodiformes, 43
Amblypygi, 31
Amblystoma, see *Ambystoma*
Ambystoma, Ambystomoidea, 40
Ambystomoidea, 40
*Ameiurus, Siluroidea, 37
American badger (*Taxidea*),
     Fissipeda, 45
American 'buffalo' (*Bison*),
     Ruminantia, 46
American 'elk' (*Cervus*), Ruminantia, 46
American flying squirrel (*Glaucomys*),
     Sciuromorpha, 45
American ground squirrel (*Citellus*),
     Sciuromorpha, 45
American opossum (*Didelphis*),
     Marsupialia, 44
American whelk (*Busycon*), Stenoglossa, 22
Ametabola, see Apterygota
Amia, Protospondyli, 36
*Ammocoetes, Hyperoartii, 35
Amoeba, Amoebina, 7
amoebic dysentery (*Entamoeba*),
     Amoebina, 7
Amoebina, 7
Amoebosporidia, see Cnidosporidia
*Amorpha, Ditrysia, 28
Ampharete, Polychaeta, 24
*Amphelocheirus,[1] see *Aphelocheirus*
Amphibia, 40–41
amphibious leech (*Trocheta*),
     Gnathobdellida, 24
Amphicoela, 40
Amphidiscophora, 10
*Amphidromus, Stylommatophora, 22
Amphileptus, Rhabdophorina, 8
Amphilina, Amphilinidea, 14
Amphilinidea, 14
Amphineura, 21 (footnote)
Amphinome, Polychaeta, 24
Amphioxus, see *Branchiostoma*
Amphipholis, Ophiurae, 34
Amphipnous, Synbranchoidea, 40
Amphipoda, 30
Amphiporus, Monostylifera, 16
*Amphisbetia, Thecata, 11
*Amphitrite, Polychaeta, 24
*—, see *Portunus*

---

[1] *Amphelocheirus* is a misprint for *Aphelocheirus*, not a synonym. As synonyms, preceded by an equals sign, are put in brackets after the correct name, misprints such as *Amphelocheirus* are not mentioned after the correct name.

Aphredoderus, Salmopercae, 37
Aphrocallistes, Hexasterophora, 10
Aphrodite, Polychaeta, 24
*Aphrophora, Homoptera, 27
Apis, Apocrita, 29
Apistobuthus, Scorpiones, 31
Aplacophora, 21
Aplidium, Aplousobranchiata, 34
*Aplodinotus, Percoidea, 38
Aplodontia, Sciuromorpha, 45
Aplousobranchiata, 34
Aplysia, Pleurocoela, 22
Aplysilla, Keratosa, 10
Aplysina, Keratosa, 10
Apocrita, 29
Apoda, 33
—, see Gymnophiona
Apodemus, Myomorpha, 45
Apodes, 37
Apodiformes, 43
Aporhynchus, Tetrarhynchoidea, 14
*Aporia, Ditrysia, 28
Aporrhais, Mesogastropoda, 22
Apostomatida, 8
*Apotettix, Caelifera, 27
Appendicularia, Copelata, 35
Apseudes, Tanaidacea, 30
Aptenodytes, Sphenisciformes, 42
Aptera, see Diplura
Apterygiformes, 41
Apterygota, 25–26
Apteryx, Apterygiformes, 41
Apus, Apodiformes, 43
—, see *Triops*
*Aquila, Falconiformes, 42
Arachnida, 31
*Arachnomorpha, Polyphaga, 28
Arachnula, Testacea, 7
Araeolaimoidea, 19
Aramus, Gruiformes, 42
Araneae, 31
Araneus, Araneae, 31
Arapaima, Osteoglossoidea, 36
Arbacia, Arbacioida, 33
Arbacioida, 33
Arca, Filibranchia, 22
Arcella, Testacea, 7
Archaeogastropoda, 21
Archiacanthocephala, 20
Archiannelida, 24
*Archidoris, Nudibranchia, 22
Archigregarina, 7
*Archilochus, Apodiformes, 43

Architeuthis, Decapoda, 23
Archostemata, 28
*Arctia, Ditrysia, 28
*Arctocebus, Prosimii, 44
*Arctocephalus, Pinnipedia, 46
Arctomys, see *Marmota*
Ardea, Ciconiiformes, 42
Ardeiformes, see Ciconiiformes
Arenicola, Polychaeta, 24
Areosoma, Echinothurioida, 33
Argas, Acari, 31
Argonauta, Octopoda, 23
Argulus, Branchiura, 30
*Argyreus (= *Acidalia*), Ditrysia, 28
*Argyroneta, Araneae, 31
Argyrotheca, Terebratelloidea, 21
*Aricia, Ditrysia, 28
*—, see *Helina*
*—, see *Monetaria*
*—, see *Orbinia*
*Ariolimax, Stylommatophora, 22
Arion, Stylommatophora, 22
*Arius, Siluroidea, 37
Arixenia, Arixeniina, 27
Arixeniina, 27
Armadillidium, Isopoda, 30
armadillo (*Dasypus*), Edentata, 44
—, giant (*Priodontes*), Edentata, 44
*Arphia, Caelifera, 27
arrow worms (Chaetognatha), 32
arrow-tooth shell (*Conus*), Stenoglossa, 22
—— (*Terebra*), Stenoglossa, 22
Artemia, Anostraca, 29
Arthropleona, 25
Arthropoda, 24–32
*Artibeus, Microchiroptera, 44
Articulata, 21, 32
Artiodactyla, 46
Arvicola, Myomorpha, 45
Ascaphus, Amphicoela, 40
Ascaridia, Ascaridina, 18
Ascaridina, 18
Ascaris, Ascaridina, 18
Ascaroidea, 19
Aschelminthes, 17–18
Ascidia, Phlebobranchiata, 34
Ascidiacea, 34–35
Ascidicola, Notodelphyoida, 29
Ascidiella, Phlebobranchiata, 34
Ascoglossa, see Sacoglossa
ascon sponges (Homocoela), 9
Asconosa, 10
Ascorhynchomorpha, 32

Ascorhynchus, Ascorhynchomorpha, 32
Ascothoracica, 30
Ascute, see *Leucosolenia*
Asellus, Isopoda, 30
Asiatic elephant (*Elephas*), Proboscidea, 46
★*Asio*, Strigiformes, 43
Aspiculuris, Ascaridina, 18
Aspidobothria, see Aspidogastrea
Aspidobranchia, see Archaeogastropoda
Aspidochirota, 32
Aspidocotylea, see Aspidogastrea
Aspidogaster, Aspidogastrea, 14
Aspidogastrea, 14
Aspidosiphon, Sipunculoidea, 23
Aspiriculata, 35
Asplanchna, Ploima, 17
★*Aspredo*, Siluroidea, 37
assassin bug (*Rhodnius*), Heteroptera, 27
Assulina, Testacea, 7
Astacus, Reptantia, 31
★*Astasia*, Euglenoidina, 6
Asterias, Forcipulata, 34
Asterina, Spinulosa, 34
Asteroidea, 34
★*Asterolecanium*, Homoptera, 27
Asteronyx, Euryalae, 34
Astomatida, 8
Astrodisculus, Heliozoa, 7
Astromonaxonellida, see Hadromerina
★*Astronesthes*, Stomiatoidea, 36
Astropecten, Phanerozona, 34
Astrosclerophora, 10
★*Astroscopus*, Percoidea, 38
Astur, see *Accipiter*
Astylosternus, Diplasiocoela, 41
Asymmetron, Cephalochordata, 35
Ateleopus, Chondrobrachii, 37
Ateles, Simiae, 44
Atelostomata, 33–34
Athecanephria, 32
Athecata, 11
★*Athelges*, Isopoda, 30
Atherina, Mugiloidea, 38
Atlantic seal (*Halichoerus*), Pinnipedia, 46
atlas moth (*Attacus*), Ditrysia, 28
Atolla, Coronatae, 11
Atrax, Araneae, 31
Atremata, 21
Attacus, Ditrysia, 28
★*Attagenus*, Polyphaga, 28
Atubaria, Cephalodiscida, 34
★*Atypus*, Araneae, 31
Auchenia, see *Lama*

Aulacantha, Radiolaria, 7
Aulastoma, see *Haemopis*
Aulostomiformes, see Solenichthyes
Aurelia, Semaeostomae, 12
Aurellia, see *Aurelia*
Aves, 41–43
★*Axinella*, Sigmatosclerophora, 10
axolotl (*Siredon*), Ambystomoidea, 40
'—' (*Ambystoma*), Ambystomoidea, 40
★*Aythya* (=*Fuligula*, *Nyroca*),
    Anseriformes, 42

B

Babesia, Haemosporidia, 8
★*Babirusa*, see *Babyrousa*
baboon (*Papio*), Simiae, 44
★*Babyrousa* (=*Babirusa*), Suiformes, 46
backswimmer (*Notonecta*), Heteroptera, 27
★*Bactrurus*, see *Eucrangonyx*
badger (*Meles*), Fissipeda, 45
—, American (*Taxidea*), Fissipeda, 45
Baetis, Ephemeroptera, 26
★*Bagrus*, Siluroidea, 37
bag-worm moth (*Psyche*), Ditrysia, 28
Bajulus, Homosclerophora, 10
★*Balaena*, Mysticeti, 45
Balaeniceps, Ciconiiformes, 42
Balaenoptera, Mysticeti, 45
Balanoglossus, Enteropneusta, 34
Balantidium, Trichostomatida, 8
Balanus, Thoracica, 30
Balistes, Balistoidea, 39
Balistoidea, 39
★*Banasa*, Heteroptera, 27
bandicoot (*Perameles*), Marsupialia, 44
bank vole (*Clethrionomys*), Myomorpha, 45
barbet (*Capito*), Piciformes, 43
★*Barbulanympha*, Metamonadina, 6
★*Barbus*, Cyprinoidea, 37
Barentsia, Pedicellinidae, 20
barnacle, goose (*Lepas*), Thoracica, 30
barnacles (Thoracica), 30
★*Barnea*, Eulamellibranchia, 23
barracuda (*Sphyraena*), Mugiloidea, 38
★*Baseodiscus* (=*Polia*), Heteronemertina, 16
Basommatophora, 22
bass (*Morone*), Percoidea, 38
bat, brown (*Myotis*), Microchiroptera, 44
—, fruit (*Cynopterus*), Megachiroptera, 44
—, — (*Epomophorus*), Megachiroptera, 44
—, horseshoe (*Rhinolophus*),
    Microchiroptera, 44
bath sponge (*Spongia*), Keratosa, 10

Bathynella, Bathynellacea, 30
Bathynellacea, 30
Batoidea, 36
Batrachoidiformes, see Haplodoci
*Bdellocephala, Paludicola, 13
Bdelloidea, 17
Bdellomorpha, see Bdellonemertina
Bdellonemertina, 17
Bdellostoma, see Heptatretus
Bdelloura, Maricola, 13
beaked whale (Mesoplodon), Odontoceti, 45
bear (Ursus), Fissipeda, 45
—, polar (Thalarctos), Fissipeda, 45
beard worms (Pogonophora), 32
beaver (Castor), Sciuromorpha, 45
—, mountain (Aplodontia), Sciuromorpha, 45
bed-bug (Cimex), Heteroptera, 27
bee, bumble (Bombus), Apocrita, 29
—, honey (Apis), Apocrita, 29
bee-eater (Merops), Coraciiformes, 43
beetles (Coleoptera), 28
Belone, Scombresocoidea, 37
Beloniformes, see Synentognathi
*Belostoma, Heteroptera, 27
Beroe, Beroida, 13
Beroida, 13
Bertiella, Cyclophyllidea, 14
Berycomorphi, 38
Beryx, Berycomorphi, 38
*Betta, Anabantoidea, 38
Bettongia, Marsupialia, 44
bichir (Polypterus), Cladistia, 36
Bilharzia, see Schistosoma
Bilharziella, Digenea, 14
*Bimastus, Oligochaeta, 24
Biomyxa, Testacea, 7
Bipalium, Terricola, 13
birds (Aves), 41–43
Bison, Ruminantia, 46
bison (Bison), Ruminantia, 46
*Bispira, Polychaeta, 24
Bithynia, Mesogastropoda, 22
biting lice (Mallophaga), 27
Bittacus, Mecoptera, 28
Bivalvia, 22–23
Blaberus, Blattodea, 26
black corals (Antipatharia), 12
black fly (Simulium), Nematocera, 28
black vulture (Aegypius), Falconiformes, 42
blackbird (Turdus), Passeres, 43
black-fish (Dallia), Haplomi, 37
blackhead of poultry (Histomonas),
    Rhizomastigina, 7

Blaniulus, Julida, 25
*Blarina, Insectivora, 44
Blastodinium, Dinoflagellata, 6
Blastophaga, Apocrita, 29
Blatta, Blattodea, 26
*Blattella, Blattodea, 26
Blattodea, 26
Blennioidea, 38
Blennius, Blennioidea, 38
blenny (Blennius), Blennioidea, 38
*Blepharipoda, Reptantia, 31
*Blepharisma, Heterotrichina, 9
Blissus, Heteroptera, 27
*Blitophaga, Polyphaga, 28
blowfly (Calliphora), Cyclorrhapha, 28
bluebottle (Calliphora), Cyclorrhapha, 28
blue crab (Callinectes), Reptantia, 31
blue whale (Sibbaldus), Mysticeti, 45
boa (Constrictor), Serpentes, 41
boar-fish (Capros), Zeomorphi, 38
Bodo, Protomonadina, 6
*Boiga (= Dipsadomorphus), Serpentes, 41
Bolina, see Bolinopsis
Bolinopsis, Lobata, 12
*Bolitophila, Nematocera, 28
Boltenia, Stolidobranchiata, 35
*—, see Laevoleacina
*Bolteria, Heteroptera, 27
Bombina, Opisthocoela, 40
Bombinator, see Bombina
Bombus, Apocrita, 29
Bombyx, Ditrysia, 28
Bonellia, Echiuroinea, 23
bony fishes (Pisces), 36–40
book lice (Psocoptera), 27
boot-lace worm (Lineus),
    Heteronemertina, 16
Bopyrus, Isopoda, 30
*Borborodes, see Scymnorhinus
Boreus, Mecoptera, 28
Bos, Ruminantia, 46
*Botaurus, Ciconiiformes, 42
Bothriocephaloidea, see Pseudophyllidea
*Bothriocephalus, Pseudophyllidea, 14
Bothus, Heterosomata, 39
Botryllus, Stolidobranchiata, 35
bottle-nosed dolphin (Tursiops),
    Odontoceti, 45
Bougainvillea, Athecata, 11
Boveria, Thigmotrichida, 9
Bowerbankia, Ctenostomata, 20
bow-fins (Protospondyli), 36
Brachiata, see Pogonophora

*Chiroleptes, see Cyclorana
Chironomus, Nematocera, 28
*Chironys, see Daubentonia
Chiroptera, 44
Chiton, Chitonida, 21
Chitonida, 21
*Chlaenius, Adephaga, 28
*Chlamydodon, Cyrtophorina, 8
Chlamydomonas, Phytomonadina, 6
Chlamydophrys, Testacea, 7
*Chlamydoselachus, Notidanoidea, 35
*Chlamyphorus, Edentata, 44
*Chloeopsis, see Cloeon
*Chloraema, see Flabelligera
Chloramoeba, Xanthomonadina, 6
*Chloris, Passeres, 43
Chlorogonium, Phytomonadina, 6
*Chlorohydra, Athecata, 11
Chloromonadina, 6
Chloromyxum, Myxosporidia, 8
*Chologaster, Microcyprini, 38
Chondracanthus, Lernaeopodoida, 30
Chondrichthyes, see Selachii
Chondrobrachii, 37
Chondropterygii, see Selachii
Chondrosia, Astrosclerophora, 10
Chondrostei, 36
Chonotrichida, 8
Chordata, 34–46
Chordeuma, Nematophora, 25
Chordeumida, see Nematophora
Chordodes, Gordioidea, 17
Choristida, 11
*Chorophilus, see Pseudacris
Chorthippus, Caelifera, 27
*Chortophaga, Caelifera, 27
Chromadorida, 18
Chromadoroidea, 18
Chromulina, Chrysomonadina, 6
Chrysamoeba, Chrysomonadina, 6
Chrysaora, Semaeostomae, 12
Chrysemys, Cryptodira, 41
Chrysochloris, Insectivora, 44
Chrysolina, Polyphaga, 28
Chrysomonadina, 6
Chrysopa, Planipennia, 28
Chthamalus, Thoracica, 30
Chthonius, Pseudoscorpiones, 31
*Chydorus, Cladocera, 29
cicada (Magicicada), Homoptera, 27
*Cichla, Percoidea, 38
Cicindela, Adephaga, 28
Ciconia, Ciconiiformes, 42

Ciconiiformes, 42
Cidaris, Cidaroida, 33
Cidaroida, 33
Ciliata, 8–9
Ciliophora, see Ciliata
Cimex, Heteroptera, 27
Ciona, Phlebobranchiata, 34
*Circotettix, Caelifera, 27
*Circus, Falconiformes, 42
*Cirolana, Isopoda, 30
Cirratulus, Polychaeta, 24
Cirripedia, 30
*Cistudo, Cryptodira, 41
Citellus, Sciuromorpha, 45
civet (Viverra), Fissipeda, 45
Cladistia, 36
Cladocera, 29
Cladocopa, 29
Cladorhiza, Sigmatosclerophora, 10
*Clangula, Anseriformes, 42
*Clarias, Siluroidea, 37
Clathrina, Homocoela, 9
Clathrulina, Heliozoa, 7
*Clava, Athecata, 11
Clavelina, Aplousobranchiata, 34
clawed toad (Xenopus), Opisthocoela, 40
*Clemmys, Cryptodira, 41
Clethrionomys, Myomorpha, 45
*Clibanarius, Reptantia, 31
Climacostomum, Heterotrichina, 9
climbing perch (Anabas), Anabantoidea, 38
cling-fishes (Xenopterygii), 39
Cliona, Astrosclerophora, 10
Clione, Pteropoda, 22
Clistogastra, see Apocrita
Clitellio, Oligochaeta, 24
*Cloeon (= Chloeopsis), Ephemeroptera, 26
Clonorchis, Digenea, 14
clothes moth (Tinea), Ditrysia, 28
Clupea, Clupeoidea, 36
Clupeiformes, see Isospondyli
Clupeoidea, 36
Clypeaster, Clypeasterina, 33
Clypeasterina, 33
Clypeasteroida, 33
*Cnemidophorus, Sauria, 41
*Cnesterodon, Microcyprini, 38
Cnidaria, 11–12
—, see Ctenophora
Cnidosporidia, 8
coat of mail shell (Chiton), Chitonida, 21
cobego (Cynocephalus), Dermoptera, 44
*Cobitis, Cyprinoidea, 37

Cyclopoida, 29
Cycloposthium, Entodiniomorphida, 9
Cyclops, Cyclopoida, 29
Cyclopterus, Scorpaenoidea, 39
Cyclorana (= *Chiroleptes*), Procoela, 40
Cyclorrhapha, 28
Cyclospora, Eimeriidea, 7
Cyclostoma, see *Pomatias*
Cyclostomata, 20, 35
Cydippida, 12
Cygnus, Anseriformes, 42
Cylindroiulus, Julida, 25
Cylindrolaimus, Chromadorida, 18
Cymbium, see *Melo*
Cymothoa, Isopoda, 30
Cynips (= *Dryophanta*), Apocrita, 29
Cynocephalus, Dermoptera, 44
Cynomys, Sciuromorpha, 45
Cynopterus, Megachiroptera, 44
Cynoscion, Percoidea, 38
Cyphoderia, Testacea, 7
Cypraea, Mesogastropoda, 22
Cypridina, Myodocopa, 29
Cyprinodontes, see Microcyprini
Cyprinodontiformes, see Microcyprini
Cyprinoidea, 37
Cyprinus, Cyprinoidea, 37
Cypris, Podocopa, 29
Cyrtophorina, 8
cyst eelworm (*Heterodera*), Tylenchida, 18
Cysticercus, see *Taenia*
Cystophora, Pinnipedia, 46
Cythere, Podocopa, 29
Cytherella, Platycopa, 29
Cyzicus, Conchostraca, 29

D

Dactylifera, see Temnocephalidea
Dactyloda, see Temnocephalidea
Dactylogyrus, Gyrodactyloidea, 13
Dactylometra, Semaeostomae, 12
Dactylopteroidea, see Cephalacanthoidea
Dactylopterus, see *Cephalacanthus*
Dacus, Cyclorrhapha, 28
daddy-long-legs (*Tipula*), Nematocera, 28
Dallia, Haplomi, 37
Dallina, Terebratelloidea, 21
Dallingeria, Metamonadina, 6
Dalyellia, Rhabdocoela, 13
Dama, Ruminantia, 46
Damon, Amblypygi, 31
damsel flies (Zygoptera), 26
Danaus (= *Anosia*), Ditrysia, 28

Danio, Cyprinoidea, 37
Daphnia, Cladocera, 29
Dardanus, Reptantia, 31
Dasyatis, Batoidea, 36
Dasybranchus, Polychaeta, 24
Dasypus, Edentata, 44
Dasyurus, Marsupialia, 44
Daubentonia (= *Chironys*), Prosimii, 44
dead men's fingers (*Alcyonium*),
   Alcyonacea, 12
death's head hawk moth (*Acherontia*),
   Ditrysia, 28
Decapoda, 23, 31
Decticus, Ensifera, 26
deep-sea anglerfishes (Ceratioidea), 39
deer, fallow (*Dama*), Ruminantia, 46
—, musk (*Moschus*), Ruminantia, 46
—, red (*Cervus*), Ruminantia, 46
deer mouse (*Peromyscus*), Myomorpha, 45
Deilephila, Ditrysia, 28
Deima, Elasipoda, 32
Delphinus, Odontoceti, 45
Demospongiae, 10–11
Dendraster, Scutellina, 33
Dendrobates, Procoela, 40
Dendrochirota, 33
Dendrocoelum, Paludicola, 13
Dendroctonus, Polyphaga, 28
Dendrodoa, Stolidobranchiata, 35
Dendrohyrax, Hyracoidea, 46
Dendroides, Polyphaga, 28
Dendrolimus, Ditrysia, 28
Dendromonas, Chrysomonadina, 6
Dendrostomum, Sipunculoidea, 23
Denisonia, Serpentes, 41
Dentalium, Scaphopoda, 22
Depressaria, Ditrysia, 28
Dermanyssus, Acari, 31
Dermaptera, 27
Dermestes, Polyphaga, 28
Dermochelys, Cryptodira, 41
Dermoptera, 44
Derocheilocarida, 30
Derocheilocaris, Derocheilocarida, 30
Derostoma, Rhabdocoela, 13
Desmodus, Microchiroptera, 44
Desmognathus, Salamandroidea, 40
Desmomyaria, see Salpida
Desmoscolecoidea, 19
Desmoscolex, Chromadorida, 18
Devescovina, Metamonadina, 6
Diacrisia, Ditrysia, 28
Diadema, Diadematoida, 33

Doris, Nudibranchia, 22
dormouse (*Glis*), Myomorpha, 45
— (*Muscardinus*), Myomorpha, 45
Dorylaimina, 18
Dorylaimoidea, 18
Dorylaimus, Dorylaimina, 18
Dracunculoidea, 19
Dracunculus, Spirurida, 18
dragonets (Callionymoidea), 38
dragon-fishes (Hypostomides), 39
dragonflies, true (Anisoptera), 26
Drepanophorus, Polystylifera, 16
* *Drilocrius*, Oligochaeta, 24
dromedary (*Camelus*), Tylopoda, 46
* *Dromia*, Reptantia, 31
Dromiceius, Casuariiformes, 41
drone fly (*Eristalis*), Cyclorrhapha, 28
Drosophila, Cyclorrhapha, 28
* *Dryocopus*, Piciformes, 43
* *Dryophanta*, see *Cynips*
duck (*Anas*), Anseriformes, 42
duck-bill (*Ornithorhynchus*),
    Monotremata, 43
Dugesia, Paludicola, 13
Dugong, Sirenia, 46
dugong (*Dugong*), Sirenia, 46
dusky salamander (*Desmognathus*),
    Salamandroidea, 40
dwarf siren (*Pseudobranchus*), Meantes, 40
Dysdercus, Heteroptera, 27
dysentery (*Balantidium*),
    Trichostomatida, 8
—, amoebic (*Entamoeba*), Amoebina, 7
Dytiscus, Adephaga, 28

E

ear-shell (*Haliotis*), Archaeogastropoda, 21
earthworm (*Allolobophora*), Oligochaeta, 24
— (*Eisenia*), Oligochaeta, 24
— (*Lumbricus*), Oligochaeta, 24
— (*Pheretima*), Oligochaeta, 24
earwigs (Forficulina), 27
eastern mole (*Scalopus*), Insectivora, 44
eastern newt (*Diemictylus*),
    Salamandroidea, 40
Ebria, Ebriideae, 6
Ebriaceae, see Ebriideae
Ebriideae, 6
* *Ecdyonurus*, Ephemeroptera, 26
Echeneibothrium, Tetraphyllidea, 14
Echeneiformes, see Discocephali
Echeneis, Discocephali, 39
Echidna, see *Tachyglossus*

Echidnophaga, Siphonaptera, 29
Echinacea, 33
Echinarachnius, Scutellina, 33
Echiniscus, Heterotardigrada, 32
Echinobothrium, Diphyllidea, 14
Echinocardium, Spatangoida, 34
Echinococcus, Cyclophyllidea, 14
Echinocucumis, Dendrochirota, 33
Echinocyamus, Laganina, 33
Echinoderes, Echinoderida, 17
Echinoderida, 17
Echinodermata, 32–34
Echinoida, 33
Echinoidea, 33–34
Echinometra, Echinoida, 33
Echinoneina, 33
Echinoneus, Echinoneina, 33
Echinorhinus, Squaloidea, 36
Echinorhynchus, Palaeacanthocephala, 20
Echinosorex, Insectivora, 44
Echinostoma, Digenea, 14
Echinothurioida, 33
Echinus, Echinoida, 33
* *Echiostoma*, Stomiatoidea, 36
Echiuroidea, 23
Echiuroinea, 23
Echiurus, Echiuroinea, 23
Ectobius, Blattodea, 26
Ectoprocta, see Polyzoa
Edentata, 44
edible crab (*Cancer*), Reptantia, 31
eel, Congo (*Amphiuma*),
    Salamandroidea, 40
—, electric (*Electrophorus*), Cyprinoidea, 37
—, mud- (*Siren*), Meantes, 40
—, shore (*Alabes*), Alabetoidea, 40
eels (Apodes), 37
—, cusk (Ophidioidea), 38
—, gulper (Lyomeri), 37
—, spiny (Opisthomi), 39
eelworm, cyst (*Heterodera*), Tylenchida, 18
—, leaf (*Aphelenchoides*), Tylenchida, 18
—, root-knot (*Meloidogyne*),
    Tylenchida, 18
—, sour paste (*Panagrellus*),
    Rhabditina, 17
—, stem-and-bulb (*Ditylenchus*),
    Tylenchida, 18
—, vinegar (*Turbatrix*), Rhabditina, 17
—, wheat gall (*Anguina*), Tylenchida, 18
* *Egernia*, Sauria, 41
* *Eidolon*, Megachiroptera, 44
Eimeria, Eimeriidea, 7

fleas (Siphonaptera), 29
—, water (Cladocera), 29
flies, caddis (Trichoptera), 28
—, damsel (Zygoptera), 26
—, may- (Ephemeroptera), 26
—, scorpion (Mecoptera), 28
—, stone- (Plecoptera), 26
—, true (Diptera), 28
—, two-winged (Diptera), 28
Floriceps, Tetrarhynchoidea, 14
Floscularia, Flosculariacea, 17
—, see *Collotheca*
Flosculariacea, 17
flounder (*Limanda*), Heterosomata, 39
flour beetle (*Tribolium*), Polyphaga, 28
flour moths (*Ephestia*), Ditrysia, 28
fluke, cattle rumen (*Paramphistomum*),
	Digenea, 14
—, liver, cattle and sheep (*Dicrocoelium*),
	Digenea, 14
—, — (*Fasciola*), Digenea, 14
—, lung (*Paragonimus*), Digenea, 14
flukes (Trematoda), 14
Flustra, Cheilostomata, 20
fly, alder (*Sialis*), Megaloptera, 27
—, ant lion (*Myrmeleon*), Planipennia, 28
—, black (*Simulium*), Nematocera, 28
—, chalcid (*Chalcis*), Apocrita, 29
—, Dobson (*Corydalis*), Megaloptera, 27
—, drone (*Eristalis*), Cyclorrhapha, 28
—, frit (*Oscinella*), Cyclorrhapha, 28
—, horse (*Tabanus*), Brachycera, 28
—, house (*Musca*), Cyclorrhapha, 28
—, ichneumon (*Ichneumon*), Apocrita, 29
—, — (*Nemeritis*), Apocrita, 29
—, lantern (*Phenax*), Homoptera, 27
—, sand (*Phlebotomus*), Nematocera, 28
—, small fruit (*Drosophila*),
	Cyclorrhapha, 28
—, snake (*Raphidia*), Megaloptera, 27
—, tse-tse (*Glossina*), Cyclorrhapha, 28
flying fish (*Exocoetus*), Exocoetoidea, 37
flying fox (*Pteropus*), Megachiroptera, 44
flying gurnards (Cephalacanthoidea), 39
flying lemur (*Cynocephalus*),
	Dermoptera, 44
flying squirrel, American (*Glaucomys*),
	Sciuromorpha, 45
— —, scale-tailed (*Anomalurus*),
	Sciuromorpha, 45
Foettingeria, Apostomatida, 8
Folia, see *Velamen*
Foraminifera, 7

Forcipulata, 34
Forficula, Forficulina, 27
Forficulina, 27
Formica, Apocrita, 29
Formicarius, Tyranni, 43
four-eyed fish (*Anableps*), Microcyprini, 38
fowl (*Gallus*), Galliformes, 42
—, guinea (*Numida*), Galliformes, 42
fowl louse (*Lipeurus*), Mallophaga, 27
fox (*Vulpes*), Fissipeda, 45
—, flying (*Pteropus*), Megachiroptera, 44
Fratercula, Charadriiformes, 42
Fregata, Pelecaniformes, 42
fresh-water crayfish (*Astacus*),
	Reptantia, 31
— — (*Cambarus*), Reptantia, 31
fresh-water limpet (*Ancylus*),
	Basommatophora, 22
fresh-water shrimp (*Gammarus*),
	Amphipoda, 30
frigate bird (*Fregata*), Pelecaniformes, 42
Fringilla, Passeres, 43
frit fly (*Oscinella*), Cyclorrhapha, 28
Fritillaria, Copelata, 35
frog (*Rana*), Diplasiocoela, 41
—, hairy (*Astylosternus*), Diplasiocoela, 41
—, marsupial (*Gastrotheca*), Procoela, 40
—, New Zealand (*Leiopelma*),
	Amphicoela, 40
—, painted (*Discoglossus*), Opisthocoela, 40
—, poison (*Dendrobates*), Procoela, 40
—, robber (*Eleutherodactylus*), Procoela, 40
—, tailed (*Ascaphus*), Amphicoela, 40
—, tree (*Hyla*), Procoela, 40
—, — (*Rhacophorus*), Diplasiocoela, 41
—, true (*Rana*), Diplasiocoela, 41
frog fishes (Antennarioidea), 39
frog hopper (*Cercopis*), Homoptera, 27
— — (*Philaenus*), Homoptera, 27
frogmouth (*Podargus*),
	Caprimulgiformes, 43
Frontonia, Peniculina, 8
frost fish (*Lepidopus*), Trichiuroidea, 38
fruit bat (*Cynopterus*), Megachiroptera, 44
— — (*Epomophorus*), Megachiroptera, 44
fruit fly, small (*Drosophila*),
	Cyclorrhapha, 28
*Fulica, Gruiformes, 42
*Fuligula, see *Aythya*
Fundulus, Microcyprini, 38
Fungia, Scleractinia, 12
fungus gnat (*Sciara*), Nematocera, 28
Furnarius, Tyranni, 43

Hemigrapsus, Reptantia, 31
Hemimerina, 27
Hemimerus, Hemimerina, 27
Hemimetabola, see Palaeoptera
—, see Paraneoptera
—, see Polyneoptera
Hemimysis, Mysidacea, 30
Hemioniscus, Isopoda, 30
Hemiptera, 27
Hemithyris, Rhynchonelloidea, 21
Hemitripterus, Scorpaenoidea, 39
Henicops, Lithobiomorpha, 25
Henneguya, Myxosporidia, 8
Henricia, Spinulosa, 34
Hepatoxylon, Tetrarhynchoidea, 14
Hepatozoon, Adeleidea, 7
Hepialus, Monotrysia, 28
Heptabrachia, Thecanephria, 32
Heptatretus, Hyperotreti, 35
Heptranchias, Notidanoidea, 35
Hermaea, Sacoglossa, 22
Hermesinum, Ebriideae, 6
Hermione, Polychaeta, 24
hermit crab (*Dardanus*), Reptantia, 31
— — (*Pagurus*), Reptantia, 31
heron (*Ardea*), Ciconiiformes, 42
Herpestes, Fissipeda, 45
Herpobdella, see *Erpobdella*
herring (*Clupea*), Clupeoidea, 36
Hesperoctenes, Heteroptera, 27
Heterakis, Ascaridina, 18
Heterandria, Microcyprini, 38
Heterocoela, 9
Heterocotylea, see Monogenea
Heterodera, Tylenchida, 18
Heterodontus, Squaloidea, 36
Heterokrohnia, Chaetognatha, 32
Heteromi, 37
Heteromyota, 23
Heteronemertina, 16
Heterophyes, Digenea, 14
Heteroptera, 27
Heterosomata, 39
Heterostigmata, 25
Heterotardigrada, 32
Heteroteuthis, Decapoda, 23
Heterotrichida, 9
Heterotrichina, 9
Hexabothrium, Polystomatoidea, 14
Hexacrobylus, Aspiriculata, 35
Hexactinellida, 10
Hexadella, Homosclerophora, 10
Hexagenia, Ephemeroptera, 26

Hexagrammos (=*Labrax*),
    Scorpaenoidea, 39
Hexamastix, Metamonadina, 6
Hexamita, Distomatina, 7
Hexanchiformes, see Notidanoidea
Hexapoda, see Insecta
Hexarthra, Flosculariacea, 17
Hexasterophora, 10
Hexostoma, Diclidophoroidea, 13
Hiatella (=*Saxicava*),
    Eulamellibranchia, 23
Himantarium, Geophilomorpha, 25
Hippocampus, Solenichthyes, 38
Hippodamia, Polyphaga, 28
Hippolyte, Natantia, 31
Hippomorpha, 46
Hipponoe, see *Tripneustes*
Hippopotamus, Suiformes, 46
hippopotamus (*Hippopotamus*),
    Suiformes, 46
Hippotragus, Ruminantia, 46
Hircinia, Keratosa, 10
Hirudinea, 24
Hirudo, Gnathobdellida, 24
Hirundo, Passeres, 43
Hister, Polyphaga, 28
Histomonas, Rhizomastigina, 7
Histriobdella, Polychaeta, 24
hoatzin (*Opisthocomus*), Galliformes, 42
Hodotermes, Isoptera, 26
Hofstenia, Alloeocoela, 13
hog louse (*Haematopinus*), Anoplura, 27
Holasteroida, 34
Holectypoida, 33
Holocentrus, Berycomorphi, 38
Holocephali, 36
Holometabola, see Oligoneoptera
Holophrya, Rhabdophorina, 8
Holostei, 36
—, see Neopterygii
Holothuria, Aspidochirota, 32
Holothuroidea, 32–33
Holotricha, 8–9
Homarus, Reptantia, 31
Homo, Simiae, 44
Homocoela, 9
Homoptera, 27
Homosclerophora, 10
honey bee (*Apis*), Apocrita, 29
honey guide (*Indicator*), Piciformes, 43
hookworm (*Ancylostoma*), Strongylina, 18
— (*Necator*), Strongylina, 18
hoopoe (*Upupa*), Coraciiformes, 43

Hoplias, Cyprinoidea, 37
Hoplocarida, 30
Hoplonemertina, 16
Hoplosternum, Siluroidea, 37
Hormiphora, Cydippida, 12
horn-bill (*Buceros*), Coraciiformes, 43
Hornera, Cyclostomata, 20
hornet (*Vespa*), Apocrita, 29
horny sponges (Keratosa), 10
horse (*Equus*), Hippomorpha, 46
horse fly (*Tabanus*), Brachycera, 28
horse roundworm (*Parascaris*),
    Ascaridina, 18
horse stomach worm (*Habronema*),
    Spirurida, 18
horse-hair worms (Nematomorpha), 17
horse-mussel (*Modiolus*), Filibranchia, 22
horseshoe bat (*Rhinolophus*),
    Microchiroptera, 44
house fly (*Musca*), Cyclorrhapha, 28
house mouse (*Mus*), Myomorpha, 45
human louse (*Pediculus*), Anoplura, 27
humming-bird (*Trochilus*), Apodiformes, 43
Huso, Chondrostei, 36
Hutchinsoniella, Cephalocarida, 29
Hyaena, Fissipeda, 45
hyaena, striped (*Hyaena*), Fissipeda, 45
Hyalonema, Amphidiscophora, 10
Hyalospongiae, see Hexactinellida
Hyas, Reptantia, 31
Hybernia, see *Erannis*
Hydatina, see *Epiphanes*
Hydra, Athecata, 11
Hydractinia, Athecata, 11
Hydrobates, Procellariiformes, 42
Hydrobia, Mesogastropoda, 22
Hydrochoerus, Hystricomorpha, 45
Hydroides, Polychaeta, 24
hydroids (Hydrozoa), 11
Hydromedusae, see Hydrozoa
Hydrophilus, Polyphaga, 28
Hydropotes, Ruminantia, 46
Hydropsyche, Trichoptera, 28
Hydrous, see *Hydrophilus*
Hydrozoa, 11
Hydrurus, Chrysomonadina, 6
Hyemoschus, Ruminantia, 46
Hyla, Procoela, 40
Hylambates, Diplasiocoela, 41
Hylecoetus, Polyphaga, 28
Hylemyia, Cyclorrhapha, 28
Hylobates, Simiae, 44
Hylodes, see *Eleutherodactylus*

Hymenolepis, Cyclophyllidea, 14
Hymenoptera, 29
Hymenostomatida, 8
Hynobius, Cryptobranchoidea, 40
Hyperia, Amphipoda, 30
Hypermastigina, see Metamonadina
Hyperoartii, 35
Hyperoodon, Odontoceti, 45
Hyperotreti, 35
Hypnarce, see *Hypnos*
Hypnos (=*Hypnarce*), Narcobatoidea, 36
Hypocoma, Thigmotrichida, 9
Hypocomella, Thigmotrichida, 9
Hypogeophis, Gymnophiona, 41
Hypomesus, Salmonoidea, 36
Hypopomus, Cyprinoidea, 37
Hypostomides, 39
Hypotremata, 36
Hypotrichida, 9
Hypsibius, Eutardigrada, 32
Hypsiprymnodon, Marsupialia, 44
Hyracoidea, 46
hyrax, tree (*Dendrohyrax*), Hyracoidea, 46
Hystrichis, Dioctophymatina, 18
Hystricomorpha, 45
Hystrix, Hystricomorpha, 45

I

ibis (*Threskiornis*), Ciconiiformes, 42
Ichneumon, Apocrita, 29
ichneumon fly (*Ichneumon*), Apocrita, 29
—— (*Nemeritis*), Apocrita, 29
Ichthyomyzon, Hyperoartii, 35
Ichthyophis, Gymnophiona, 41
Ichthyophthirius, Tetrahymenina, 8
Icosteiformes, see Malacichthyes
Icosteus, Malacichthyes, 39
Idotea, Isopoda, 30
Iguana, Sauria, 41
iguana (*Iguana*), Sauria, 41
Ikeda, Heteromyota, 23
Ilyanassa, see *Nassa*
Inarticulata, 21
Incurvaria, Monotrysia, 28
Indian antelope (*Antilope*), Ruminantia, 46
Indian 'gharial' (*Gavialis*), Crocodylia, 41
Indicator, Piciformes, 43
Iniomi, 37
Insecta, 25–29
Insectivora, 44
Iodamoeba, Amoebina, 7
Ione, Isopoda, 30
Iphinoe, Cumacea, 30

Iphita, Heteroptera, 27
Ips (= *Tomicus*), Polyphaga, 28
Isopoda, 30
Isoptera, 26
Isospondyli, 36–37
Isospora, Eimeriidea, 7
Isotoma, Arthropleona, 25
Ithone, Planipennia, 28
Ixodes, Acari, 31

J

jacamar (*Galbula*), Piciformes, 43
Jacana, Charadriiformes, 42
jackal (*Canis*), Fissipeda, 45
jaguar (*Panthera*), Fissipeda, 45
Jaguarius, see *Panthera*
Japyx, Diplura, 26
Jassa, Amphipoda, 30
Jasus, Reptantia, 31
jelly fish (Scyphozoa), 11–12
jerboa (*Dipus*), Myomorpha, 45
jerboa pouched mouse (*Antechinomys*),
    Marsupialia, 44
jigger (*Tunga*), Siphonaptera, 29
jird (*Meriones*), Myomorpha, 45
John Dory (*Zeus*), Zeomorphi, 38
Julida, 25
Juliformia, 25
Julus, Julida, 25
jumping hare (*Pedetes*), Myomorpha, 45
jumping mouse (*Zapus*), Myomorpha, 45
jumping plant louse (*Psylla*), Homoptera, 27

K

kagu (*Rhynochetos*), Gruiformes, 42
kala-azar (*Leishmania*), Protomonadina, 6
Kalotermes, Isoptera, 26
Kaloula, Diplasiocoela, 41
Kamptozoa, see Entoprocta
kangaroo (*Bettongia*), Marsupialia, 44
— (*Macropus*), Marsupialia, 44
Karyolysus, Adeleidea, 7
Keratella, Ploima, 17
Keratosa, 10
kestrel (*Falco*), Falconiformes, 42
keyhole limpet (*Megathura*),
    Archaeogastropoda, 21
kidney worm, dog (*Dioctophyme*),
    Dioctophymatina, 18
killer whale (*Orcinus*), Odontoceti, 45
killifish (*Fundulus*), Microcyprini, 38
— (*Oryzias*), Microcyprini, 38
king crabs (Xiphosura), 31

kingfisher (*Alcedo*), Coraciiformes, 43
kinkajou (*Potos*), Fissipeda, 45
Kinorhyncha, see Echinoderida
kiwis (Apterygiformes), 41
Klossia, Adeleidea, 7
koala (*Phascolarctos*), Marsupialia, 44
Koenenia, Palpigradi, 31
Kolga, Elasipoda, 32
kreef (*Jasus*), Reptantia, 31
krill (Euphausiacea), 30
Kurtoidea, 38
Kurtus, Kurtoidea, 38

L

Labia, Forficulina, 27
Labidoplax, Apoda, 33
Labidura, Forficulina, 27
Labrax, see *Dicentrarchus*
—, see *Hexagrammos*
Labrus, Percoidea, 38
Lacazella, Thecideoidea, 21
Lacerta, Sauria, 41
Lacertilia, see Sauria
lacewing, brown (*Hemerobius*),
    Planipennia, 28
—, green (*Chrysopa*), Planipennia, 28
Lacuna, Mesogastropoda, 22
lady bird (*Coccinella*), Polyphaga, 28
Laevoleacina (= *Boltenia*),
    Stylommatophora, 22
Laganina, 33
Laganum, Laganina, 33
Lagidium (= *Viscaccia*),
    Hystricomorpha, 45
Lagomorpha, 45
Lagopus, Galliformes, 42
Lama, Tylopoda, 46
Lamellibranchia, see Bivalvia
Lamellisabella, Thecanephria, 32
Lamna, Galeoidea, 36
Lamniformes, see Galeoidea
Lampanyctus, Myctophoidea, 37
Lampetra, Hyperoartii, 35
lampreys (Hyperoartii), 35
Lampridiformes, see Allotriognathi
Lampris, Allotriognathi, 38
Lampyris, Polyphaga, 28
lancelet (*Branchiostoma*),
    Cephalochordata, 35
land snail (*Helix*), Stylommatophora, 22
land-slug (*Arion*), Stylommatophora, 22
— (*Limax*), Stylommatophora, 22
langouste (*Palinurus*), Reptantia, 31

langur (*Presbytis*), Simiae, 44
lantern fly (*Phenax*), Homoptera, 27
lantern-fish (*Lampanyctus*),
    Myctophoidea, 37
— (*Myctophum*), Myctophoidea, 37
large roundworm (*Ascaris*), Ascaridina, 18
lark (*Alauda*), Passeres, 43
Laro-Limicolae, see Charadriiformes
Larus, Charadriiformes, 42
Larvacea, 35
*Lascoderma, see Lasioderma
*Lasioderma, Polyphaga, 28
*Lasius, Apocrita, 29
*Laspeyresia (=Carpocapsa), Ditrysia, 28
*Lateolabrax, Percoidea, 38
Latimeria, Actinistia, 40
*Latreutes, Natantia, 31
Latrodectus, Araneae, 31
Laura, Ascothoracica, 30
leaf eelworm (*Aphelenchoides*),
    Tylenchida, 18
leaf-hopper (*Empoasca*), Homoptera, 27
—, sugar cane (*Perkinsiella*),
    Homoptera, 27
leaf-insect (*Phyllium*), Phasmida, 26
Leander, see *Palaemon*
leathery turtle (*Dermochelys*),
    Cryptodira, 41
Lebistes, Microcyprini, 38
Lecane, Ploima, 17
Lecanicephala, 16
Lecanicephaloidea, 14
Lecanicephalum, Lecanicephaloidea, 14
Lecudina, Eugregarina, 7
leech, amphibious (*Trocheta*),
    Gnathobdellida, 24
leeches (Hirudinea), 24
*Leimonia (=Limonia), Ditrysia, 28
Leiopelma, Amphicoela, 40
*Leipoa (=Lipoa), Galliformes, 42
Leishmania, Protomonadina, 6
lemming (*Lemmus*), Myomorpha, 45
Lemmus, Myomorpha, 45
Lemur, Prosimii, 44
lemur, common (*Lemur*), Prosimii, 44
—, flying (*Cynocephalus*), Dermoptera, 44
Lemuroidea, see Prosimii
Lensia, Siphonophora, 11
Leo, see *Panthera*
leopard (*Panthera*), Fissipeda, 45
Lepadella, Ploima, 17
Lepadogaster, Xenopterygii, 39
Lepas, Thoracica, 30

Lepidochiton, Chitonida, 21
Lepidochitona, see *Lepidochiton*
*Lepidononotus, Polychaeta, 24
Lepidopleurida, 21
Lepidopleurus, Lepidopleurida, 21
Lepidoptera, 28
Lepidopus, Trichiuroidea, 38
*Lepidorhinus, see Centrophorus
Lepidosiren, Dipnoi, 40
Lepidosteus, see *Lepisosteus*
Lepidurus, Notostraca, 29
Lepisma, Thysanura, 26
Lepisosteiformes, see Ginglymodi
Lepisosteus, Ginglymodi, 36
Leptasterias, Forcipulata, 34
Leptinotarsa, Polyphaga, 28
Leptocardii, see Cephalochordata
Leptochelia, Tanaidacea, 30
*Leptodius, Reptantia, 31
Leptodora, Cladocera, 29
*Leptograpsus, Reptantia, 31
Leptomedusae, see Thecata
Leptomonas, Protomonadina, 6
*Leptophlebia, Ephemeroptera, 26
Leptostraca, 30
Leptosynapta, Apoda, 33
Leptotheca, Myxosporidia, 8
Lepus, Lagomorpha, 45
—, see *Oryctolagus*
Lernaea, Cyclopoida, 29
—, see *Lernaeocera*
Lernaeocera, Caligoida, 29
—, see *Lernaea*
*Lernaeodiscus, Rhizocephala, 30
Lernaeopodoida, 30
lesser anteater (*Tamandua*), Edentata, 44
lesser octopus (*Eledone*), Octopoda, 23
Lestes, Zygoptera, 26
Lestris, see *Stercorarius*
Leucandra, see *Leuconia*
*Leucichthys, Salmonoidea, 36
Leucilla, Heterocoela, 9
*Leuciscus, Cyprinoidea, 37
*Leuckartiara (=Turris), Athecata, 11
Leucocytozoon, Haemosporidia, 8
Leuconia, Heterocoela, 9
*Leucophaea, Blattodea, 26
*Leucorrhinia, Anisoptera, 26
Leucosolenia, Homocoela, 9
Leucothea, Lobata, 12
Libellula, Anisoptera, 26
*Libinia, Reptantia, 31
lice (Phthiraptera), 27

lice, biting (Mallophaga), 27
—, book (Psocoptera), 27
—, sucking (Anoplura), 27
Lichenopora, Cyclostomata, 20
Licnophora, Licnophorina, 9
Licnophorina, 9
Ligia, Isopoda, 30
Ligula, Pseudophyllidea, 14
lily trotter (*Jacana*), Charadriiformes, 42
Limacina, Pteropoda, 22
Limacomorpha, see Glomeridesmida
Limanda, Heterosomata, 39
Limapontia, Sacoglossa, 22
Limax, Stylommatophora, 22
Limicolae, 24 (footnote)
Limnadia, Conchostraca, 29
Limnaea, see *Lymnaea*
Limnephilus, Trichoptera, 28
Limnocnida, Limnomedusae, 11
Limnodrilus, Oligochaeta, 24
Limnodynastes, Procoela, 40
Limnomedusae, 11
Limnoria, Isopoda, 30
Limonia, Nematocera, 28
*—, see *Leimonia*
Limosa, Charadriiformes, 42
limpet (*Acmaea*), Archaeogastropoda, 21
— (*Patella*), Archaeogastropoda, 21
—, fresh-water (*Ancylus*),
    Basommatophora, 22
—, keyhole (*Megathura*),
    Archaeogastropoda, 21
—, slipper (*Crepidula*), Mesogastropoda, 22
limpkin (*Aramus*), Gruiformes, 42
Limulida, see Xiphosura
Limulus, Xiphosura, 31
Lina, see *Melasoma*
Lineus, Heteronemertina, 16
Linguatula, Porocephalida, 32
Lingula, Atremata, 21
Linognathus, Anoplura, 27
Linuche, Coronatae, 11
lion (*Panthera*), Fissipeda, 45
—, Californian sea (*Zalophus*),
    Pinnipedia, 46
—, mountain (*Felis*), Fissipeda, 45
—, sea (*Otaria*), Pinnipedia, 46
Liopelma, see *Leiopelma*
Liopeltis, Serpentes, 41
Lipeurus, Mallophaga, 27
Lipoa, see *Leipoa*
Lipotropha, Schizogregarina, 7
Liriope, Trachymedusae, 11

Lirus, Stromateoidea, 38
Lithobiomorpha, 25
Lithobius, Lithobiomorpha, 25
Lithodes, Reptantia, 31
Litomastix, Apocrita, 29
Littorina, Mesogastropoda, 22
liver fluke, cattle and sheep (*Dicrocoelium*),
    Digenea, 14
— — (*Fasciola*), Digenea, 14
lizard, green (*Lacerta*), Sauria, 41
—, wall (*Lacerta*), Sauria, 41
lizard-fish (*Synodus*), Myctophoidea, 37
lizards (Sauria), 41
llama (*Lama*), Tylopoda, 46
Loa, Spirurida, 18
Lobata, 12
lobster (*Homarus*), Reptantia, 31
—, Norway (*Nephrops*), Reptantia, 31
—, rock (*Panulirus*), Reptantia, 31
locust (*Locusta*), Caelifera, 27
— (*Schistocerca*), Caelifera, 27
—, grouse (*Tetrix*), Caelifera, 27
Locusta, Caelifera, 27
loggerhead sponge (*Spheciospongia*),
    Astrosclerophora, 10
Loligo, Decapoda, 23
Lomechusa, Polyphaga, 28
long necked turtle (*Chelodina*),
    Pleurodira, 41
longhorned grasshoppers (Ensifera), 26
Lophiiformes, see Pediculati
Lophioidea, 39
Lophiomys, Myomorpha, 45
Lophius, Lophioidea, 39
Lophogaster, Mysidacea, 30
Lophohelia, Scleractinia, 12
Lophomonas, Metamonadina, 6
Lophopanopeus, Reptantia, 31
Lophopoda, see Phylactolaemata
Lophoproctus, Polyxenida, 24
Lophortyx, Galliformes, 42
Lophosaura, see *Microsaura*
Loricaria, Siluroidea, 37
Loricata, see Crocodylia
—, see Polyplacophora
Loricati, see Scleroparei
Loris, Prosimii, 44
loris (*Loris*), Prosimii, 44
Lota, Anacanthini, 38
Lottia, Archaeogastropoda, 21
louse, crab (*Phthirus*), Anoplura, 27
—, elephant (*Haematomyzus*),
    Rhynchophthirina, 27

Maricola, 13
marmoset (*Hapale*), Simiae, 44
marmot (*Marmota*), Sciuromorpha, 45
Marmota, Sciuromorpha, 45
Marsipobranchii, 35
marsupial frog (*Gastrotheca*), Procoela, 40
Marsupialia, 44
marten (*Martes*), Fissipeda, 45
Martes, Fissipeda, 45
Marthasterias, Forcipulata, 34
Mastacembeliformes, see Opisthomi
Mastacembelus, Opisthomi, 39
Mastigamoeba, Rhizomastigina, 7
Mastigias, Rhizostomae, 12
Mastigophora, 6–7
Mastigoproctus, Uropygi, 31
Mastomys, Myomorpha, 45
Mastotermes, Isoptera, 26
matamata (*Chelus*), Pleurodira, 41
may-flies (Ephemeroptera), 26
Mazama, Ruminantia, 46
Mazocraes, Diclidophoroidea, 13
mealworm (*Tenebrio*), Polyphaga, 28
Meandrina, Scleractinia, 12
Meantes, 40
Mecistocephalus, Geophilomorpha, 25
Mecoptera, 28
medaka (*Oryzias*), Microcyprini, 38
medusae (Hydrozoa), 11
Megacephalum, see *Macrocephalon*
Megachiroptera, 44
Megalobatrachus, Cryptobranchoidea, 40
Megalops, Clupeoidea, 36
Megaloptera, 27
Meganyctiphanes, Euphausiacea, 30
megapode (*Megapodius*), Galliformes, 42
Megapodius, Galliformes, 42
Megaptera, Mysticeti, 45
Megathura, Archaeogastropoda, 21
Megophrys, Anomocoela, 40
Melanocetus, Ceratioidea, 39
Melanoplus, Caelifera, 27
Melanotus, Polyphaga, 28
Melasoma (=*Lina*), Polyphaga, 28
Meleagris, Galliformes, 42
Meles, Fissipeda, 45
Melicerta, see *Floscularia*
Melittobia, Apocrita, 29
Mellita, Scutellina, 33
Melo (=*Cymbium*), Stenoglossa, 22
Meloidogyne, Tylenchida, 18
Melolontha, Polyphaga, 28
Melophagus, Cyclorrhapha, 28

Melopsittacus, Psittaciformes, 43
Membranipora, Cheilostomata, 20
Menippe, Reptantia, 31
Menopon, Mallophaga, 27
Menura, Menurae, 43
Menurae, 43
Mergus, Anseriformes, 42
Meriones, Myomorpha, 45
Merluccius, Anacanthini, 38
Mermis, Dorylaimina, 18
Mermithoidea, 18
Merocystis, Eimeriidea, 7
Merogregarina, Archigregarina, 7
Merops, Coraciiformes, 43
Merostomata, 31
Mesidotea, Isopoda, 30
Mesocestoides, Cyclophyllidea, 14
Mesocricetus, Myomorpha, 45
Mesoenas, Gruiformes, 42
Mesogastropoda, 22
Mesonemertina, see Palaeonemertina
Mesoplodon, Odontoceti, 45
Mesothuria, Aspidochirota, 32
Mesozoa, 9
Mespilia, Temnopleuroida, 33
Messor, Apocrita, 29
Metabola, see Pterygota
Metachirus, Marsupialia, 44
Metacrinus, Articulata, 32
Metamonadina, 6
Metastrongylus, Strongylina, 18
Metatheria, 44
Metopidia, see *Lepadella*
Metridium, Actiniaria, 12
Mexican digger toad (*Rhinophrynus*),
    Procoela, 40
Microbisium, Pseudoscorpiones, 31
Microchiroptera, 44
Microchordeuma, Nematophora, 25
Microciona, Sigmatosclerophora, 10
Microcotyle, Diclidophoroidea, 13
Microcyema, Dicyemida, 9
Microcyprini, 38
Microdina, see *Philodinavus*
Microdipodops, Sciuromorpha, 45
Microgromia, Testacea, 7
Microhyla, Diplasiocoela, 41
Micromys, Myomorpha, 45
Micronecta, Heteroptera, 27
Micronematus, see *Pristiphora*
Microphis, Solenichthyes, 38
Micropleura, Spirurida, 18
Micropodiformes, see Apodiformes

Micropogon, Percoidea, 38
Micropterus, Percoidea, 38
Micropteryx, Zeugloptera, 28
Micropus, see *Apus*
Microsaura (=*Lophosaura*), Sauria, 41
Microsclerophora, see Homosclerophora
Microsporidia, 8
Microstomum, Rhabdocoela, 13
Microthelyphonida, see Palpigradi
Microtus, Myomorpha, 45
micro-whip scorpions (Palpigradi), 31
midge, pear (*Contarinia*), Nematocera, 28
midwife toad (*Alytes*), Opisthocoela, 40
Miliola, Foraminifera, 7
Millepora, Athecata, 11
miller's thumb (*Cottus*), Scorpaenoidea, 39
millipedes (Diplopoda), 24–25
Milnesium, Eutardigrada, 32
mink (*Mustela*), Fissipeda, 45
minnow (*Phoxinus*), Cyprinoidea, 37
Miripinnati, 37
Mirounga, Pinnipedia, 46
mite (*Acarus*), Acari, 31
— (*Dermanyssus*), Acari, 31
— (*Pyemotes*), Acari, 31
— (*Trombicula*), Acari, 31
Mithrax, Reptantia, 31
Mnemiopsis, Lobata, 12
Modiolus, Filibranchia, 22
Moina, Cladocera, 29
Mola, Tetraodontoidea, 39
Molanna, Trichoptera, 28
mole, common old world (*Talpa*),
     Insectivora, 44
—, eastern (*Scalopus*), Insectivora, 44
—, golden (*Chrysochloris*), Insectivora, 44
mole cricket (*Gryllotalpa*), Ensifera, 26
mole mouse (*Mystromys*),
     Myomorpha, 45
mole rat (*Spalax*), Myomorpha, 45
mole salamander (*Ambystoma*),
     Ambystomoidea, 40
Molgula, Stolidobranchiata, 35
Mollusca, 21–23
Molothrus (=*Agelaioides*), Passeres, 43
Molpadia, Molpadonia, 33
Molpadonia, 33
Momotus, Coraciiformes, 43
Monas, Protomonadina, 6
Monaxonida, 11
Monetaria (=*Aricia*),
     Mesogastropoda, 22
mongoose (*Herpestes*), Fissipeda, 45

Monhystera, Chromadorida, 18
Monhysteroidea, 19
Moniezia, Cyclophyllidea, 14
Moniliformis, Archiacanthocephala, 20
monkey, spider (*Ateles*), Simiae, 44
—, squirrel (*Saimiri*), Simiae, 44
monkeys, African tree (*Cercopithecus*),
     Simiae, 44
Monocelis, Alloeocoela, 13
Monocentris, Berycomorphi, 38
Monocercomonas, Metamonadina, 6
Monocystis, Eugregarina, 7
Monodella, Thermosbaenacea, 30
Monogenea, 13–14
Monogononta, 17
Monomastigocystis, Heliozoa, 7
Mononchus, Enoplina, 18
Monopisthocotylea, 13
Monoplacophora, 21
Monoraphis, Amphidiscophora, 10
Monosiga, Protomonadina, 6
Monostyla, Ploima, 17
Monostylifera, 16
Monotocardia, see Mesogastropoda
Monotremata, 43
Monotrysia, 28
Monstrilla, Monstrilloida, 29
Monstrilloida, 29
moon rat (*Echinosorex*), Insectivora, 44
moon-fish (*Lampris*), Allotriognathi, 38
moose (*Alces*), Ruminantia, 46
moray (*Muraena*), Apodes, 37
Mormoniella, Apocrita, 29
Mormyroidea, 37
Morone, Percoidea, 38
Moschus, Ruminantia, 46
mosquito (*Anopheles*), Nematocera, 28
— (*Culex*), Nematocera, 28
Motacilla, Passeres, 43
Motella, see Gaidropsarus
moth, atlas (*Attacus*), Ditrysia, 28
—, bag-worm (*Psyche*), Ditrysia, 28
—, clothes (*Tinea*), Ditrysia, 28
—, death's head hawk (*Acherontia*),
     Ditrysia, 28
—, ghost (*Hepialus*), Monotrysia, 28
—, gipsy (*Lymantria*), Ditrysia, 28
—, goat (*Cossus*), Ditrysia, 28
—, pine shoot (*Evetria*), Ditrysia, 28
—, silk (*Bombyx*), Ditrysia, 28
—, wax (*Galleria*), Ditrysia, 28
moths, flour (*Ephestia*), Ditrysia, 28
motmot (*Momotus*), Coraciiformes, 43

mountain beaver (*Aplodontia*),
    Sciuromorpha, 45
mountain lion (*Felis*), Fissipeda, 45
mouse, deer (*Peromyscus*), Myomorpha, 45
—, house (*Mus*), Myomorpha, 45
—, jerboa pouched (*Antechinomys*),
    Marsupialia, 44
—, jumping (*Zapus*), Myomorpha, 45
—, mole (*Mystromys*), Myomorpha, 45
—, wood (*Apodemus*), Myomorpha, 45
mouse birds (Coliiformes), 43
mouse pinworm (*Aspiculuris*),
    Ascaridina, 18
— threadworm (*Aspiculuris*), Ascaridina, 18
Mrazekia, Microsporidia, 8
mud-eel (*Siren*), Meantes, 40
mud-minnow (*Umbra*), Haplomi, 37
mud-puppy (*Necturus*), Proteida, 40
mud-skipper (*Periophthalmus*),
    Gobioidea, 38
Muellerius, Strongylina, 18
Muggiaea, Siphonophora, 11
Mugil, Mugiloidea, 38
Mugiloidea, 38
Mulinia, Eulamellibranchia, 23
mullets, grey (Mugiloidea), 38
multimammate rat (*Mastomys*),
    Myomorpha, 45
Munida, Reptantia, 31
Muraena, Apodes, 37
Murex, Stenoglossa, 22
Murgantia, Heteroptera, 27
Mus, Myomorpha, 45
Musca, Cyclorrhapha, 28
Muscardinus, Myomorpha, 45
musk deer (*Moschus*), Ruminantia, 46
musk ox (*Ovibos*), Ruminantia, 46
muskrat (*Ondatra*), Myomorpha, 45
Musophaga, Cuculiformes, 43
mussel (*Mytilus*), Filibranchia, 22
—, horse- (*Modiolus*), Filibranchia, 22
—, pearl- (*Unio*), Eulamellibranchia, 23
—, swan- (*Anodonta*), Eulamellibranchia, 23
Mustela, Fissipeda, 45
Mustelus, Galeoidea, 36
Mya, Eulamellibranchia, 23
Myctophoidea, 37
Myctophum, Myctophoidea, 37
Myliobatis, Batoidea, 36
Myocastor, Hystricomorpha, 45
Myodocopa, 29
Myomorpha, 45
Myosoma, Pedicellinidae, 20

Myotis, Microchiroptera, 44
Myoxocephalus, Scorpaenoidea, 39
Myoxus, see *Glis*
Myrientomata, see Protura
Myrmecophaga, Edentata, 44
Myrmeleon, Planipennia, 28
Myrmica, Apocrita, 29
Mysidacea, 30
Mysis, Mysidacea, 30
Mystacocarida, 30
Mysticeti, 45
Mystromys, Myomorpha, 45
Mytilus, Filibranchia, 22
Myxidium, Myxosporidia, 8
Myxilla, Sigmatosclerophora, 10
Myxine, Hyperotreti, 35
Myxini, see Hyperotreti
Myxobolus, Myxosporidia, 8
Myxochloris, Xanthomonadina, 6
Myxosoma, Myxosporidia, 8
Myxospongida, 10
Myxosporidia, 8
Myzostoma, Myzostomaria, 24
Myzostomaria, 24

N

nagana (*Trypanosoma*), Protomonadina, 6
Naja, Serpentes, 41
Narcacion, see *Torpedo*
Narcine, Narcobatoidea, 36
Narcobatoidea, 36
Narcobatus, see *Torpedo*
Narcomedusae, 11
Nassa, Stenoglossa, 22
Nassarius, Stenoglossa, 22
Nassula, Cyrtophorina, 8
Nasua, Fissipeda, 45
Natalobatrachus, see *Phrynobatrachus*
Natantia, 31
Natica, Mesogastropoda, 22
'native cat' (*Dasyurus*), Marsupialia, 44
Natrix, Serpentes, 41
Nausithoe, Coronatae, 11
Nautilus, Tetrabranchia, 23
nautilus, paper- (*Argonauta*), Octopoda, 23
—, pearly- (*Nautilus*), Tetrabranchia, 23
Neanthes, Polychaeta, 24
Nebalia, Nebaliacea, 30
Nebaliacea, 30
Nebela, Testacea, 7
Necator, Strongylina, 18
necklace-shell (*Natica*), Mesogastropoda, 22
— (*Strombus*), Mesogastropoda, 22

Nectonema, Nectonematoidea, 17
Nectonematoidea, 17
Nectonemertes, Polystylifera, 16
*Nectophrynoides, Procoela, 40
Necturus, Proteida, 40
Neelus, Symphypleona, 25
Nemata, see Nematoda
Nemathelminthes, 17 (footnote)
Nematocera, 28
Nematocystida, see Cnidosporidia
Nematoda, 17–18
*Nematodinium, Dinoflagellata, 6
Nematognathi, see Siluroidea
Nematomorpha, 17
Nematophora, 25
Nematus, Symphyta, 29
Nemeritis, Apocrita, 29
Nemertina, 16–17
Nemobius, Ensifera, 26
Nemoura, Plecoptera, 26
Neoceratodus, Dipnoi, 40
Neodasys, Chaetonotoidea, 17
Neoechinorhynchus, Eoacanthocephala, 20
Neogastropoda, see Stenoglossa
Neolampas, Nucleolitoida, 33
Neomenia, Neomeniomorpha, 21
Neomeniomorpha, 21
Neopilina, Tryblidiacea, 21
Neoptera, 26–29
Neopterygii, 36–40
Neosporidia, see Cnidosporidia
Neotermes, Isoptera, 26
Neotremata, 21
*Neoturris (=Turris), Athecata, 11
*Nepa, Heteroptera, 27
Nephelis, see Erpobdella
*Nephelopteryx, Plecoptera, 26
Nephrops, Reptantia, 31
Nephthys, Polychaeta, 24
*Neptunea, Stenoglossa, 22
Nereis, Polychaeta, 24
Nerilla, Archiannelida, 24
Nerita, Archaeogastropoda, 21
*Neritina, Archaeogastropoda, 21
*Nerocila, Isopoda, 30
*Nerophis, Solenichthyes, 38
Nestor, Psittaciformes, 43
Neuroptera, 27–28
New Zealand frog (Leiopelma),
    Amphicoela, 40
newt (Triturus), Salamandroidea, 40
—, eastern (Diemictylus),
    Salamandroidea, 40

newt, pleurodele (Pleurodeles),
    Salamandroidea, 40
nightjar (Caprimulgus),
    Caprimulgiformes, 43
*Niphargus, Amphipoda, 30
*Nippostrongylus, Strongylina, 18
Nippotaenia, Nippotaenoidea, 14
Nippotaeniidea, 16
Nippotaenoidea, 14
Noah's ark shell (Arca),
    Filibranchia, 22
Noctiluca, Dinoflagellata, 6
*Noctua (=Phalaena), Ditrysia, 28
nodular worm (Oesophagostomum),
    Strongylina, 18
Nomeus, Stromateoidea, 38
Norway lobster (Nephrops),
    Reptantia, 31
Nosema, Microsporidia, 8
*Nosopsyllus, Siphonaptera, 29
Notacanthiformes, see Heteromi
Notacanthus, Heteromi, 37
Notaspidea, 22
Nothoprocta, Tinamiformes, 41
Nothura, Tinamiformes, 41
Notidanoidea, 35
Notidanus, Notidanoidea, 35
Notodelphyoida, 29
*Notomastus, Polychaeta, 24
Notommata, Ploima, 17
Notonecta, Heteroptera, 27
Notoplana, Acotylea, 13
Notoptera, see Grylloblattodea
Notopteroidea, 37
Notopterus, Notopteroidea, 37
*Notornis, Gruiformes, 42
*Notoryctes, Marsupialia, 44
*Notostira, Heteroptera, 27
Notostraca, 29
Nototrema, see Gastrotheca
*Nucella (=Purpura), Stenoglossa, 22
Nucleolitoida, 33
Nucula, Protobranchia, 22
Nuda, 9–10, 13
Nudibranchia, 22
*Numenius, Charadriiformes, 42
Numida, Galliformes, 42
Nummulites, Foraminifera, 7
nut-shell (Nucula), Protobranchia, 22
*Nycticebus, Prosimii, 44
Nymphon, Nymphonomorpha, 32
Nymphonomorpha, 32
*Nyroca, see Aythya

O

Obelia, Thecata, 11
Ocenebra, Stenoglossa, 22
Ochetostoma, Echiuroinea, 23
Ochotona, Lagomorpha, 45
Ochromonas, Chrysomonadina, 6
Octocorallia, 12
Octopoda, 23
Octopus, Octopoda, 23
octopus (*Octopus*), Octopoda, 23
—, lesser (*Eledone*), Octopoda, 23
Octospinifer, Eoacanthocephala, 20
Ocypode, Reptantia, 31
Odobenus, Pinnipedia, 46
Odocoileus, Ruminantia, 46
Odonata, 26
Odontaspis, Galeoidea, 36
Odontoceti, 45
Odontopyge, Spirostreptida, 25
Odontostomatida, see Ctenostomatida
Odontosyllis, Polychaeta, 24
Oecanthus, Ensifera, 26
Oedemia, see *Oidemia*
Oesophagostomum, Strongylina, 18
Oicomonas, Chrysomonadina, 6
Oidemia (= *Oedemia*), Anseriformes, 42
Oikopleura, Copelata, 35
oil bird (*Steatornis*), Caprimulgiformes, 43
Oiphysa, Homoptera, 27
okapi (*Okapia*), Ruminantia, 46
Okapia, Ruminantia, 46
Oligobrachia, Athecanephria, 32
Oligochaeta, 24
Oligolophus, Opiliones, 31
Oligoneoptera, 27–29
Oligotoma, Embioptera, 27
Oligotrichida, 9
Olindias, Limnomedusae, 11
olm (*Proteus*), Proteida, 40
olympic salamander (*Rhyacotriton*),
    Ambystomoidea, 40
Ommastrephes (= *Ommatostrephes*),
    Decapoda, 23
Ommatostrephes, see *Ommastrephes*
Onchidella, see *Oncidiella*
Onchidium, see *Oncidium*
Onchidoris, Nudibranchia, 22
Onchocerca, Spirurida, 18
Oncicola, Archiacanthocephala, 20
Oncidiella (= *Onchidella*),
    Stylommatophora, 22
Oncidium (= *Onchidium*),
    Stylommatophora, 22

Oncopeltus, Heteroptera, 27
Oncorhynchus, Salmonoidea, 36
Ondatra, Myomorpha, 45
Oniscomorpha, see Glomerida
Oniscus, Isopoda, 30
Onos, see *Gaidropsarus*
Onychophora, 24
Ooencyrtus, Apocrita, 29
Opalina, Opalinina, 7
Opalinina, 7
Ophelia, Polychaeta, 24
Ophiactis, Ophiurae, 34
Ophicephaloidea, see Channoidea
Ophicephalus, see *Channa*
Ophidia, see Serpentes
Ophidioidea, 38
Ophiocomina, Ophiurae, 34
Ophiodon, Scorpaenoidea, 39
Ophiopholis, Ophiurae, 34
Ophiopsila, Ophiurae, 34
Ophiothrix, Ophiurae, 34
Ophisaurus, Sauria, 41
Ophiura, Ophiurae, 34
Ophiurae, 34
Ophiuraespira, Apostomatida, 8
Ophiuroidea, 34
Ophryocystis, Schizogregarina, 7
Ophryoscolex, Entodiniomorphida, 9
Ophyra, Cyclorrhapha, 28
Opiliones, 31
Opisthandria, see Pentazonia
Opisthobranchia, 22
Opisthocoela, 40
Opisthocomus, Galliformes, 42
Opisthomi, 39
Opisthophthalmus, Scorpiones, 31
opossum, American (*Didelphis*),
    Marsupialia, 44
opossum-shrimps (Mysidacea), 30
Opsanus, Haplodoci, 39
orang (*Pongo*), Simiae, 44
Orasema, Apocrita, 29
Orbinia (= *Aricia*), Polychaeta, 24
Orchesella, Arthropleona, 25
Orcinus, Odontoceti, 45
Orectolobus, Galeoidea, 36
oriental sore (*Leishmania*),
    Protomonadina, 6
ormer (*Haliotis*), Archaeogastropoda, 21
Ornithodoros, Acari, 31
Ornithorhynchus, Monotremata, 43
Orthagoriscus, see *Mola*
Orthomorpha, Polydesmida, 25

Orthonectida, 9
Orthoptera, 26–27
Orya, Geophilomorpha, 25
Orycteropus, Tubulidentata, 46
Oryctes, Polyphaga, 28
Oryctolagus, Lagomorpha, 45
Oryzias, Microcyprini, 38
Oscanius, see *Pleurobranchus*
Oscarella, Homosclerophora, 10
Oscinella, Cyclorrhapha, 28
Oscines, see Passeres
Osilinus, Archaeogastropoda, 21
Osmerus, Salmonoidea, 36
Osphronemus, Anabantoidea, 38
osprey (*Pandion*), Falconiformes, 42
Ostariophysi, 37
Osteichthyes, see Pisces
Osteoglossoidea, 36
Ostertagia, Strongylina, 18
Ostracoda, 29
Ostrea, Eulamellibranchia, 23
ostriches (Struthioniformes), 41
Otaria, Pinnipedia, 46
Otis, Gruiformes, 42
Otomesostoma, Alloeocoela, 13
Otostigmus, Scolopendromorpha, 25
otter (*Lutra*), Fissipeda, 45
Otus, Strigiformes, 43
ovenbird (*Furnarius*), Tyranni, 43
Ovibos, Ruminantia, 46
Ovis, Ruminantia, 46
Owenia, Polychaeta, 24
owls (Strigiformes), 43
ox, musk (*Ovibos*), Ruminantia, 46
Oxidus, Polydesmida, 25
Oxycarenus, Heteroptera, 27
Oxynotus (= *Centrina*), Squaloidea, 36
Oxytricha, Hypotrichida, 9
Oxyuris, Ascaridina, 18
Oxyuroidea, 19
oyster (*Ostrea*), Eulamellibranchia, 23
—, saddle- (*Anomia*), Filibranchia, 22

P

Pachybolus, Spirobolida, 25
Pachygrapsus, Reptantia, 31
Pachyiulus, Julida, 25
Pachypalaminus, Cryptobranchoidea, 40
Pacific giant salamander (*Dicamptodon*),
    Ambystomoidea, 40
paddle-fish (*Polyodon*), Chondrostei, 36
Pagrosomus, Percoidea, 38
Paguristes, Reptantia, 31

Pagurus, Reptantia, 31
—, see *Dardanus*
painted frog (*Discoglossus*),
    Opisthocoela, 40
Palaeacanthocephala, 20
Palaemon, Natantia, 31
—, see *Macrobrachium*
Palaeonemertina, 16
Palaeoptera, 26
—, see Paraneoptera
—, see Polyneoptera
Palaeopterygii, 36
Palinurus, Reptantia, 31
Palmipes, see *Anseropoda*
Palpigradi, 31
Paludicola, 13
Paludina, see *Viviparus*
Palythoa, Zoanthiniaria, 12
Pan, Simiae, 44
Panagrellus, Rhabditina, 17
Pancarida, 30
panda (*Ailurus*), Fissipeda, 45
—, giant (*Ailuropoda*), Fissipeda, 45
Pandalus, Natantia, 31
Pandinus, Scorpiones, 31
Pandion, Falconiformes, 42
Pandorina, Phytomonadina, 6
pangolin (*Manis*), Pholidota, 44
Panorpa, Mecoptera, 28
Panorpatae, see Mecoptera
panther (*Panthera*), Fissipeda, 45
Panthera, Fissipeda, 45
Pantopoda, see Pycnogonida
Pantostomatida, see Rhizomastigina
Panulirus, Reptantia, 31
paper-nautilus (*Argonauta*),
    Octopoda, 23
Papilio, Ditrysia, 28
Papio, Simiae, 44
Parabrotula, Ophidioidea, 38
Paracanthonchus, Chromadorida, 18
Paracentrotus, Echinoida, 33
Paragonimus, Digenea, 14
Paralepis, Alepisauroidea, 37
Paralichthys, Heterosomata, 39
Paralithodes, Reptantia, 31
Paramecium, Peniculina, 8
Paramphistomum, Digenea, 14
Paraneoptera, 27
—, see Palaeoptera
—, see Polyneoptera
Paraneuroptera, see Odonata
Parascaris, Ascaridina, 18

Pyromelana, see *Euplectes*
Pyrophorus, Polyphaga, 28
Pyrosoma, Pyrosomida, 35
Pyrosomida, 35
Pyrrhocoris, Heteroptera, 27
Python, Serpentes, 41
python (*Python*), Serpentes, 41
Pyura, Stolidobranchiata, 35

Q

Quadrigyrus, Eoacanthocephala, 20
quetzal (*Pharomachrus*), Trogoniformes, 43
quokka (*Setonyx*), Marsupialia, 44

R

rabbit (*Oryctolagus*), Lagomorpha, 45
rabbit-fishes (Holocephali), 36
raccoon (*Procyon*), Fissipeda, 45
Radiolaria, 7
Radiophrya, Astomatida, 8
rag-fishes (Malacichthyes), 39
rail (*Rallus*), Gruiformes, 42
Raillietina, Cyclophyllidea, 14
Raja, Batoidea, 36
Rallus, Gruiformes, 42
Ramphastos, Piciformes, 43
ram's horn snail (*Planorbis*),
    Basommatophora, 22
Rana, Diplasiocoela, 41
Randallia, Reptantia, 31
Rangifer, Ruminantia, 46
Raniceps, Anacanthini, 38
Raphidia, Megaloptera, 27
Raphidiophrys, Heliozoa, 7
rat (*Rattus*), Myomorpha, 45
—, cotton (*Sigmodon*), Myomorpha, 45
—, coucha (*Mastomys*), Myomorpha, 45
—, maned (*Lophiomys*), Myomorpha, 45
—, mole (*Spalax*), Myomorpha, 45
—, moon (*Echinosorex*), Insectivora, 44
—, multimammate (*Mastomys*),
    Myomorpha, 45
rat-kangaroo (*Potorous*), Marsupialia, 44
rattle snake (*Crotalus*), Serpentes, 41
Rattulus, see *Trichocerca*
Rattus, Myomorpha, 45
raven (*Corvus*), Passeres, 43
ray (*Raja*), Batoidea, 36
—, sting (*Dasyatis*), Batoidea, 36
rays (Hypotremata), 36
razorbill (*Alca*), Charadriiformes, 42
red deer(*Cervus*), Ruminantia, 46
Reduvius, Heteroptera, 27

reed-fish (*Calamoichthys*), Cladistia, 36
Reighardia, Cephalobaenida, 32
reindeer (*Rangifer*), Ruminantia, 46
Reithrodontomys, Myomorpha, 45
Remora, Discocephali, 39
Reniera, see *Adocia*
Renilla, Pennatulacea, 12
Reptantia, 31
reptiles (Reptilia), 41
Reptilia, 41
Rhabdias, Rhabditina, 17
Rhabdiasoidea, 19
Rhabditida, 17–18
Rhabditina, 17
Rhabditis, Rhabditina, 17
Rhabditoidea, 19
Rhabdocoela, 13
Rhabdophaga, Nematocera, 28
Rhabdophorina, 8
Rhabdopleura, Rhabdopleurida, 34
Rhabdopleurida, 34
Rhabdostyla, Peritrichida, 9
Rhachianectes, Mysticeti, 45
Rhacophorus, Diplasiocoela, 41
Rhagio, Brachycera, 28
Rhea, Rheiformes, 41
rheas (Rheiformes), 41
Rhegnopteri, see Polynemoidea
Rheiformes, 41
Rhineura, Sauria, 41
Rhinobatus, Batoidea, 36
Rhinoceros, Ceratomorpha, 46
rhinoceros (*Ceratotherium*),
    Ceratomorpha, 46
— (*Diceros*), Ceratomorpha, 46
— (*Rhinoceros*), Ceratomorpha, 46
Rhinochimaera, Holocephali, 36
Rhinocricus, Spirobolida, 25
Rhinoderma, Diplasiocoela, 41
Rhinolophus, Microchiroptera, 44
Rhinophrynus, Procoela, 40
Rhithropanopeus, Reptantia, 31
Rhizocephala, 30
Rhizochloris, Xanthomonadina, 6
Rhizocrinus, Articulata, 32
Rhizomastigina, 7
Rhizopoda, 7
Rhizostoma, Rhizostomae, 12
Rhizostomae, 12
Rhodites, see *Diplolepis*
Rhodnius, Heteroptera, 27
Rhodosoma, Phlebobranchiata, 34
Rhomboidichthys, Heterosomata, 39